# Resource File
## with Answer Key

## Holt Social Studies

# Europe and Russia

**HOLT, RINEHART AND WINSTON**

A Harcourt Education Company

Orlando • **Austin** • New York • San Diego • Toronto • London

ISBN 0-03-078606-1

5 6 7  018  08

# Early History of Europe

Contents

**Vocabulary Builder**
Section 1.................................................................1
Section 2.................................................................2
Section 3.................................................................3

**Biography**
Alexander the Great .......................................................4
Octavia Thurina Minor ....................................................6

**Literature**
"The Knight's Tale" from *The Canterbury Tales* by Geoffrey Chaucer.................8

**Primary Source**
*The Deeds of the Divine Augustus*.........................................10

**Geography and History**
Rome's Trade Routes, First Century AD....................................12

**Social Studies Skills**
Interpreting a Historical Map .............................................14

**Geography for Life**
Transportation in Europe: Then and Now...................................15

**Critical Thinking**
The Roads of Ancient Rome ...............................................18

**Focus on Reading**
Re-reading ...............................................................20

**Focus on Writing**
Writing a Myth ...........................................................22

**Chapter Review**.........................................................24

**Interdisciplinary Project**
Research Project: The Black Death ........................................26
Handout 1: Assignment A: The Black Death Basics .........................28
Handout 2: Assignment B: Battling the Black Death .......................29
Handout 3: Assignment C: The Black Death's Path..........................30
Rubric: Standards for Evaluating Your Work...............................31

**Answer Key** ............................................................228

# History of Early Modern Europe

**Vocabulary Builder**
Section 1 . . . . . . . . . . . . . . . . . . . . . . . . . . . . . . . . . . . . . . . . . . . . . . . 32
Section 2 . . . . . . . . . . . . . . . . . . . . . . . . . . . . . . . . . . . . . . . . . . . . . . . 33
Section 3 . . . . . . . . . . . . . . . . . . . . . . . . . . . . . . . . . . . . . . . . . . . . . . . 34
Section 4 . . . . . . . . . . . . . . . . . . . . . . . . . . . . . . . . . . . . . . . . . . . . . . . 35

**Biography**
Galileo . . . . . . . . . . . . . . . . . . . . . . . . . . . . . . . . . . . . . . . . . . . . . . . . 36
Napoleon Bonaparte . . . . . . . . . . . . . . . . . . . . . . . . . . . . . . . . . . . . . 38

**Literature**
*Frankenstein* by Mary Wollstonecraft Shelley . . . . . . . . . . . . . . . . . . 40

**Primary Source Activity**
The Notebooks of Leonardo da Vinci . . . . . . . . . . . . . . . . . . . . . . . . . 42

**Geography and History**
Magellan's Voyage around the World . . . . . . . . . . . . . . . . . . . . . . . . . 44

**Social Studies Skills**
Making Economic Choices . . . . . . . . . . . . . . . . . . . . . . . . . . . . . . . . . 46

**Geography for Life**
Italian Renaissance Cities: A Modern Way of Life? . . . . . . . . . . . . . . 47

**Critical Thinking**
The Industrial Revolution: Two Viewpoints . . . . . . . . . . . . . . . . . . . . 50

**Focus on Reading**
Understanding Chronological Order . . . . . . . . . . . . . . . . . . . . . . . . . . 52

**Focus on Writing**
Creating a Travel Brochure . . . . . . . . . . . . . . . . . . . . . . . . . . . . . . . . 53

**Chapter Review** . . . . . . . . . . . . . . . . . . . . . . . . . . . . . . . . . . . . . . . . . . 55

**Answer Key** . . . . . . . . . . . . . . . . . . . . . . . . . . . . . . . . . . . . . . . . . . . . . 230

**Vocabulary Builder**
Section 1. . . . . . . . . . . . . . . . . . . . . . . . . . . . . . . . . . . . . . . . . . . . . . . . . .57
Section 2. . . . . . . . . . . . . . . . . . . . . . . . . . . . . . . . . . . . . . . . . . . . . . . . . .58
Section 3. . . . . . . . . . . . . . . . . . . . . . . . . . . . . . . . . . . . . . . . . . . . . . . . . .59

**Biography**
Anne Frank . . . . . . . . . . . . . . . . . . . . . . . . . . . . . . . . . . . . . . . . . . . . . . .60
Vladimir Lenin . . . . . . . . . . . . . . . . . . . . . . . . . . . . . . . . . . . . . . . . . . . .62

**Literature**
*Animal Farm* by George Orwell. . . . . . . . . . . . . . . . . . . . . . . . . . . . . . .64

**Primary Source**
Charter of the United Nations. . . . . . . . . . . . . . . . . . . . . . . . . . . . . . . .66

**Geography and History**
Europe and World War I . . . . . . . . . . . . . . . . . . . . . . . . . . . . . . . . . . . .68

**Social Studies Skills**
Interpreting Political Cartoons . . . . . . . . . . . . . . . . . . . . . . . . . . . . . . .70

**Geography for Life**
The Soviet "Game of the Name" . . . . . . . . . . . . . . . . . . . . . . . . . . . . . .71

**Critical Thinking**
Disaster at Chernobyl. . . . . . . . . . . . . . . . . . . . . . . . . . . . . . . . . . . . . . .74

**Focus on Reading**
Using Context Clues–Contrast . . . . . . . . . . . . . . . . . . . . . . . . . . . . . . .76

**Focus on Writing**
Writing a Diary Entry. . . . . . . . . . . . . . . . . . . . . . . . . . . . . . . . . . . . . . .78

**Chapter Review**. . . . . . . . . . . . . . . . . . . . . . . . . . . . . . . . . . . . . . . . . . . .80

**Interdisciplinary Projects**
Reading and Writing Allegories. . . . . . . . . . . . . . . . . . . . . . . . . . . . . . .82
Handout: Writing Your Allegory . . . . . . . . . . . . . . . . . . . . . . . . . . . . . .84
Rubric: Standards for Evaluating Your Work . . . . . . . . . . . . . . . . . . . .85
Current Events: Letting Historical Figures Solve Today's Problems . . . . . . . . . . . . . .86

**Answer Key** . . . . . . . . . . . . . . . . . . . . . . . . . . . . . . . . . . . . . . . . . . . . . . .233

# Southern Europe

**Vocabulary Builder**

Section 1............................................88

Section 2............................................89

Section 3............................................90

Section 4............................................91

**Biography**

Aristotle............................................92

Amália Rodrigues...................................94

**Literature**

Don Quixote by Miguel de Cervantes..............96

**Primary Source**

"The Creation of Adam" by Michelangelo..........98

**Geography and History**

Northern and Southern Italy.....................100

**Social Studies Skills**

Reading a Climate Map...........................102

**Geography for Life**

The Mediterranean Sea...........................103

**Critical Thinking**

Is Venice Slipping Away?.........................106

**Focus on Reading**

Asking Questions.................................108

**Focus on Writing**

Writing a News Report............................109

**Chapter Review**.................................111

**Answer Key**....................................236

# Contents

**Vocabulary Builder**

Section 1. . . . . . . . . . . . . . . . . . . . . . . . . . . . . . . . . . . . . . . . . . . . . . . . . . . .113

Section 2. . . . . . . . . . . . . . . . . . . . . . . . . . . . . . . . . . . . . . . . . . . . . . . . . . . .114

Section 3. . . . . . . . . . . . . . . . . . . . . . . . . . . . . . . . . . . . . . . . . . . . . . . . . . . .115

**Biography**

Jacques-Yves Cousteau . . . . . . . . . . . . . . . . . . . . . . . . . . . . . . . . . . . . . . . .116

Emmy Noether . . . . . . . . . . . . . . . . . . . . . . . . . . . . . . . . . . . . . . . . . . . . . . .118

**Literature**

*The Lily of the Valley* by Honoré de Balzac. . . . . . . . . . . . . . . . . . . . . . . . . . .120

**Primary Source**

"Above the Clouds, the French Glimpse the Old Grandeur" by Elaine Sciolino . . . . . .122

**Geography and History**

Countries in the European Union. . . . . . . . . . . . . . . . . . . . . . . . . . . . . . . . . .124

**Social Studies Skills**

Analyzing a Circle Graph. . . . . . . . . . . . . . . . . . . . . . . . . . . . . . . . . . . . . . . .126

**Geography for Life**

The EU and NATO: Past, Present, and Future. . . . . . . . . . . . . . . . . . . . . . . . .127

**Critical Thinking**

A Taste of France. . . . . . . . . . . . . . . . . . . . . . . . . . . . . . . . . . . . . . . . . . . . . .130

**Focus on Reading**

Recognizing Word Origins. . . . . . . . . . . . . . . . . . . . . . . . . . . . . . . . . . . . . . .132

**Focus on Speaking**

Presenting a Persuasive Speech . . . . . . . . . . . . . . . . . . . . . . . . . . . . . . . . . . .134

**Chapter Review**. . . . . . . . . . . . . . . . . . . . . . . . . . . . . . . . . . . . . . . . . . . . . . .136

**Answer Key** . . . . . . . . . . . . . . . . . . . . . . . . . . . . . . . . . . . . . . . . . . . . . . . . . .239

Europe and Russia

# Northern Europe

Contents

**Vocabulary Builder**
Section 1 .................................................. 138
Section 2 .................................................. 139
Section 3 .................................................. 140

**Biography**
Mary, Queen of Scots ..................................... 141
Hans Christian Andersen .................................. 143

**Literature**
*Romeo and Juliet* by William Shakespeare ................. 145

**Primary Source**
"The Scream" by Edvard Munch ........................... 147

**Geography and History**
Understanding Northern Europe ........................... 149

**Social Studies Skills**
Writing to Learn ......................................... 151

**Geography for Life**
The Vikings Abroad ....................................... 152

**Critical Thinking**
Connecting Europe by Chunnel ........................... 155

**Focus on Reading**
Using Context Clues–Synonyms ........................... 157

**Focus on Writing**
Writing a Letter .......................................... 159

**Chapter Review** ......................................... 161

**Answer Key** ............................................ 241

Europe and Russia

**Vocabulary Builder**
Section 1. . . . . . . . . . . . . . . . . . . . . . . . . . . . . . . . . . . . . . . . . . . . . . . . . . . . . . . . .163
Section 2. . . . . . . . . . . . . . . . . . . . . . . . . . . . . . . . . . . . . . . . . . . . . . . . . . . . . . . . .164
Section 3. . . . . . . . . . . . . . . . . . . . . . . . . . . . . . . . . . . . . . . . . . . . . . . . . . . . . . . . .165
Section 4. . . . . . . . . . . . . . . . . . . . . . . . . . . . . . . . . . . . . . . . . . . . . . . . . . . . . . . . .166

**Biography**
Estée Lauder . . . . . . . . . . . . . . . . . . . . . . . . . . . . . . . . . . . . . . . . . . . . . . . . . . . . .167
Madeleine Albright. . . . . . . . . . . . . . . . . . . . . . . . . . . . . . . . . . . . . . . . . . . . . . . . .169

**Literature**
*The Bridge on the Drina* by Ivo Andric . . . . . . . . . . . . . . . . . . . . . . . . . . . . . . . .171

**Primary Source**
The 1956 Hungarian Revolution . . . . . . . . . . . . . . . . . . . . . . . . . . . . . . . . . . . . . .173

**Geography and History**
Soviet Domination of Eastern Europe . . . . . . . . . . . . . . . . . . . . . . . . . . . . . . . . .175

**Social Studies Skills**
Analyzing Benefits and Costs. . . . . . . . . . . . . . . . . . . . . . . . . . . . . . . . . . . . . . . . .177

**Geography for Life**
Cities and Rivers in Eastern Europe . . . . . . . . . . . . . . . . . . . . . . . . . . . . . . . . . . .178

**Critical Thinking**
Ethnic Cleansing in Bosnia . . . . . . . . . . . . . . . . . . . . . . . . . . . . . . . . . . . . . . . . . .181

**Focus on Reading**
Understanding Problems and Solutions. . . . . . . . . . . . . . . . . . . . . . . . . . . . . . . . .183

**Focus on Viewing**
Presenting and Viewing Visual Reports . . . . . . . . . . . . . . . . . . . . . . . . . . . . . . . . .185

**Chapter Review**. . . . . . . . . . . . . . . . . . . . . . . . . . . . . . . . . . . . . . . . . . . . . . . . . .187

**Teacher's Interdisciplinary Project**
Research Project: Eastern Europe's Economy. . . . . . . . . . . . . . . . . . . . . . . . . . . . .189
Handout 1: Industrial Economy . . . . . . . . . . . . . . . . . . . . . . . . . . . . . . . . . . . . . .191
Handout 2: Tourist Economy . . . . . . . . . . . . . . . . . . . . . . . . . . . . . . . . . . . . . . . .192
Handout 3: Business Plans: Improve the Economy. . . . . . . . . . . . . . . . . . . . . . . . .193
Rubric: Standards for Evaluating Your Work . . . . . . . . . . . . . . . . . . . . . . . . . . . . .194

**Answer Key** . . . . . . . . . . . . . . . . . . . . . . . . . . . . . . . . . . . . . . . . . . . . . . . . . . . . .244

# Russia and the Caucasus

**Vocabulary Builder**
Section 1. . . . . . . . . . . . . . . . . . . . . . . . . . . . . . . . . . . . . . . . . . . . . . .195
Section 2. . . . . . . . . . . . . . . . . . . . . . . . . . . . . . . . . . . . . . . . . . . . . . .196
Section 3. . . . . . . . . . . . . . . . . . . . . . . . . . . . . . . . . . . . . . . . . . . . . . .197
Section 4. . . . . . . . . . . . . . . . . . . . . . . . . . . . . . . . . . . . . . . . . . . . . . .198

**Biography**
Catherine the Great . . . . . . . . . . . . . . . . . . . . . . . . . . . . . . . . . . . . . .199
Garry Kasparov . . . . . . . . . . . . . . . . . . . . . . . . . . . . . . . . . . . . . . . . . .201

**Literature**
*War and Peace* by Leo Tolstoy . . . . . . . . . . . . . . . . . . . . . . . . . . . . . .203

**Primary Source**
Russian Icon Painting . . . . . . . . . . . . . . . . . . . . . . . . . . . . . . . . . . . . .205

**Geography and History**
Serfdom in Russia, 1860 . . . . . . . . . . . . . . . . . . . . . . . . . . . . . . . . . . .207

**Social Studies Skills**
Interpreting a Population Map . . . . . . . . . . . . . . . . . . . . . . . . . . . . . . .209

**Geography for Life**
Agriculture and Environment in the Caucasus . . . . . . . . . . . . . . . . . .210

**Critical Thinking**
A Russian Space Mystery . . . . . . . . . . . . . . . . . . . . . . . . . . . . . . . . . . .213

**Focus on Reading**
Making Generalizations . . . . . . . . . . . . . . . . . . . . . . . . . . . . . . . . . . . .215

**Focus on Writing**
Creating a Real Estate Ad . . . . . . . . . . . . . . . . . . . . . . . . . . . . . . . . . .217

**Chapter Review** . . . . . . . . . . . . . . . . . . . . . . . . . . . . . . . . . . . . . . . . .219

**Teacher's Interdisciplinary Project**
The Russian Space Program. . . . . . . . . . . . . . . . . . . . . . . . . . . . . . . . .221
Student Handout 1: Student Activity Outline . . . . . . . . . . . . . . . . . . .223
Student Handout 2: The Importance of Space Exploration . . . . . . . . .224
Student Handout 3: Comparing World Space Exploration . . . . . . . . . .225
Rubric: Standards for Evaluating Your Work . . . . . . . . . . . . . . . . . . . .226

**Answer Key** . . . . . . . . . . . . . . . . . . . . . . . . . . . . . . . . . . . . . . . . . . . .247

Europe and Russia

Name _____ Class _____ Date _____

## Early History of Europe

# Vocabulary Builder

| | | | |
|---|---|---|---|
| city-states | golden age | Athens | empire |
| Sparta | Hellenistic | colonies | |

**DIRECTIONS** On the line provided before each statement, write **T** if the statement is true and **F** if the statement is false. If the statement is false, write the correct term on the line after each sentence that makes the sentence a true statement.

_____ **1.** <u>City-states</u> are political units made up of a city and all the surrounding lands.

_____

_____ **2.** A period in a society's history marked by great achievements is called a/an <u>empire</u>.

_____

_____ **3.** <u>Sparta</u> was a city-state in eastern Greece that led the fight against the invading Persians around 500 BC.

_____

_____ **4.** A Greek-like blended culture is also called <u>Sparta</u>.

_____

_____ **5.** Because of overcrowding, Greek city-states set up new cities, or <u>colonies</u>, around the Mediterranean and Black seas.

_____

**Early History of Europe**

# Vocabulary Builder

### Section 2

| | | | |
|---|---|---|---|
| aqueducts | Carthage | citizens | Colosseum |
| empire | facilitate | Pax Romana | republic |
| Rome | Senate | | |

**DIRECTIONS** Read each sentence and fill in the blank with the word in the word pair that best completes the sentence.

**1.** The city of _____ is thought to have been set up in 753 BC by a group called the Latins. (**Rome/Carthage**)

**2.** The _____ was made up of rich and powerful Romans who helped run the city. (**Pax Romana/Senate**)

**3.** _____ were people who could take part in Rome's government. (**Citizens/Aqueducts**)

**4.** A _____ is a form of government that has the people vote for leaders to make the laws. (**Senate/republic**)

**5.** Under Octavian's leadership, Rome became a/an _____, a land that included many different peoples under one rule. (**republic/empire**)

**6.** In addition to roads and bridges, Roman engineers built

_____, channels used to carry water over long distances.

(**aqueducts/Pax Romana**)

**7.** The long period of peace and achievement that Rome experienced is called the

_____. (**Pax Romana/Colosseum**)

**DIRECTIONS** Choose five of the words from the word bank. On a separate sheet of paper, use these words to write a poem or short story that relates to the section.

**Early History of Europe**

# Vocabulary Builder

### Section 3

| | | | |
|---|---|---|---|
| Crusade | feudal system | Gothic architecture | Holy Land |
| Magna Carta | manor | Middle Ages | peasant |
| pope | serf | nation-state | |

**DIRECTIONS** Read each sentence and fill in the blank with the word in the word pair that best completes the sentence.

1. The _____ is the time period between ancient and modern times, which lasted from about 500 to 1500. (**Middle Ages/Magna Carta**)

2. The head of the Christian church is called the _____. (**manor/pope**)

3. A religious war is called a _____. (**Crusade/Holy Land**)

4. The pope wanted Europeans to take over the _____, the region where Jesus had lived. (**Crusade/Holy Land**)

5. Many churches in the Middle Ages are examples of _____, a style known for its high pointed ceilings, tall towers, and stained glass windows. (**feudal system/Gothic architecture**)

6. The system of trading land for military service is called the _____. (**feudal system/serf**)

7. A _____ is a large estate owned by a noble or knight. (**peasant/manor**)

8. A _____ is a country that is united under a single strong government. (**Holy Land/nation-state**)

**DIRECTIONS** What would your life be like if you lived in the Middle Ages? Write a letter to a friend and describe what it's like to live in the Middle Ages using five of the words in the word bank.

Name _____ Class _____ Date _____

# Alexander the Great
## c. 356–323 BC

**HOW HE AFFECTED THE WORLD**
Alexander the Great was a respected and successful emperor, commander, explorer, scholar, and politician. He founded over 70 cities and expanded his empire to stretch across three continents—about two million square miles! He was the first person in history to unite all of Greece.

*As you read the biography below,* think about how Alexander the Great's strong will and intelligence helped him lead successful conquests and grow his empire.

**VOCABULARY**
**rhetoric** the art or science of using words effectively
**assassinated** murdered
**allegiance** loyalty
**conquest** the act of getting possession or control
**champion** to advocate, or push for

Alexander the Great only lived to be 33 years old. But he accomplished much in his short lifetime.

Alexander was born in the northern Greek kingdom of Macedonia. He studied **rhetoric**, literature, science, medicine, and philosophy with the famed Greek philosopher Aristotle.

When Alexander's father, King Philip II of Macedon, went to battle in 340 BC, Alexander was left in command of Macedonia at age 16. In 336 BC, King Philip II was **assassinated** at his daughter Cleopatra's wedding. The Greek army proclaimed Alexander the new king. He was just 20.

Some parts of Greece, such as Athens, were not willing to pledge their **allegiance** to the new king. So Alexander set out to destroy his known and potential enemies. He led his army south to gain control of Greece.

After claiming victory over Greece, Alexander led his loyal, well-trained army to battle and conquer other parts of the world, including Central Asia and Egypt. His army faced overwhelming odds when he

## Alexander the Great, *continued*     Biography

fought the Persian Empire. But his army was never defeated.

Alexander's many **conquests** spread Greek culture throughout his empire. To **champion** Greek culture, Alexander encouraged Greeks to move to the new lands. He also built about 70 new cities, using Greek cities as models. Many of these new cities were named Alexandria in his honor. One of them, Alexandria in Egypt, became a leading center of learning in the ancient world.

In 323 BC, Alexander the Great was planning to expand his empire even more. He had pushed his troops into India, but they revolted. Returning to Babylon, Alexander became ill and died. He was only 33, but he had ruled over one of the greatest empires in history.

## WHAT DID YOU LEARN?

**1. Recall** How did Alexander the Great become king at age 20?

_____

_____

**2. Evaluate** What qualities do you think Alexander the Great possessed to be such a successful leader?

_____

_____

## ACTIVITY

Do more research on the conquests of Alexander the Great. Create a time line or chart showing four of the conquests that were essential to expanding Alexander's empire.

# Octavia Thurina Minor
## c. 69–11 BC

**HOW SHE AFFECTED THE REGION**
Octavia Thurina Minor is an important woman in Roman history. She was known for her kindness, loyalty, and dignity. She was one of the first Roman women to have coins made in her image. Her brother, Augustus, declared her a goddess after she died and built the Gate of Octavia in her memory.

© The Granger Collection, New York

 *As you read the biography below, think about Octavia's strength and courage during a time of political upheaval.*

Octavia Thurina Minor was born in Nola, a city in southern Italy. Not much is known about her childhood. Octavia came from an important family. Her uncle was Julius Caesar, and her brother was Augustus—the future Roman emperor.

Around 54 BC, her stepfather set up an arranged marriage for Octavia. Her husband was a **consul** in the Roman Empire. He was also a member of an important Roman family. Octavia's husband died after they had three children together.

At the time, Rome was ruled by three leaders. One was Octavia's brother, Augustus; another was Mark Antony. These two rulers were often in conflict. It was hoped that if Octavia married Mark Antony, these conflicts would end. The Roman Senate arranged for Octavia to marry Mark Antony. The marriage was a kind of political **alliance**. Octavia worked hard to help them resolve their conflicts. She succeeded, but just for a short while. She also continued to raise her three children and Mark Antony's children.

**VOCABULARY**

**upheaval** a sudden, violent change

**consul** the highest elected office of the Roman Republic

**alliance** a union for a common objective or goal

**traitor** someone who is disloyal to the government

**portico** porch or walkway with columns that support the roof

Octavia did her best to help Mark Antony rule. Once, while he was away fighting, she went to him with extra troops and money. She also tried to maintain the peace between Mark Antony and her brother.

However, Mark Antony had become involved with Cleopatra, Queen of Egypt. Many Romans now considered Mark Antony a **traitor**. In 32 BC, Mark Antony divorced Octavia. He later committed suicide in 30 BC. Octavia never remarried.

After one of Octavia's sons died, she lost interest in Rome's politics. Octavia died in 11 BC, but her contributions lived on. In honor of his beloved sister, Augustus built temples and monuments in her name, including the **Portico** of Octavia—which still stands today.

## WHAT DID YOU LEARN?

**1. Recall** Why was Octavia considered a kind woman?

_____

_____

**2. Evaluate** Why do you think marriages were arranged in the Roman Empire?

_____

_____

## ACTIVITY

Imagine you were hired by one of Mark Antony or Octavia's children to create another monument to honor Octavia's character. Draw or explain what the monument will look like.

**Early History of Europe**                                    Literature

# "The Knight's Tale"

from *The Canterbury Tales* by Geoffrey Chaucer

**ABOUT THE READING** *The Canterbury Tales* is the story of a group of 30 people who travel to Canterbury, England. These pilgrims come from various backgrounds. They tell stories to pass the time while they travel to Canterbury. The excerpt you are about to read is a portion of "The Knight's Tale."

**VOCABULARY**
**chivalry**  knightly qualities
**realm**  a kingdom
**wrought**  formed
**remnant**  what is left over
**lamentation**  expression of grief, such as crying

*As you read the passage below,* pay attention to the grand description of Theseus's conquests around the world.

Once on a time, as old stories tell to us,
There was a duke whose name was Theseus:
Of Athens he was lord and governor,
And in his time was such a conqueror
   That greater was there not beneath the sun.
Very many rich countries had he won;
What with his wisdom and his **chivalry**
He gained the **realm** of Femininity,
That was of old time known as Scythia.
   There he married the queen, Hippolyta,
And brought her home with him to his country.
In glory great and with great ceremony,
And, too, her younger sister, Emily.
And thus, in victory and with melody,
   Let I this noble duke to Athens ride
With all his armed host marching at his side.
And truly, were it not too long to hear,
I would have told you fully how, that year,
Was gained the realm of Femininity
   By Theseus and by his chivalry;

> Why do you think the queen agreed to marry Theseus?
>
> _____
> _____

And all of the great battle that was **wrought**
Where Amazons and the Athenians fought;
And how was wooed and won Hippolyta,
That fair and hardy queen of Scythia;
   And of the feast was made at their wedding,
And of the tempest at their home-coming;
But all of that I must for now forbear.
I have, God knows, a large field for my share,
And weak the oxen, and the soil is tough.

   The **remnant** of the tale is long enough.
I will not hinder any, in my turn;
Let each man tell his tale, until we learn
Which of us all the most deserves to win;
So where I stopped, again I'll now begin.
This duke of whom I speak, of great renown,
When he had drawn almost unto the town,
In all well-being and in utmost pride,
He grew aware, casting his eyes aside,
That right upon the road, as suppliants do,
   A company of ladies, two by two,
Knelt, all in black, before his cavalcade;
But such a clamorous cry of woe they made
That in the whole world living man had heard
No such a **lamentation**, on my word . . .

> Who do you think is the narrator of this tale?
>
> _____
>
> _____

## ANALYZING LITERATURE

1. **Main Idea**  Who was Theseus?

   _____

   _____

2. **Critical Thinking: Comparison**  Compare and contrast Theseus and Alexander the
   Great. Be sure to give examples.

   _____

   _____

## ACTIVITY

Write a poem or story about a notable figure you've studied in this chapter.
Model your poem or story after Chaucer's tale from *The Canterbury Tales.*

# The Deeds of the Divine Augustus

**ABOUT THE READING** Augustus, also known as Octavian, was a determined ruler. He led his legions, or soldiers, to many victories, expanding the Roman Empire to include most of Europe, as well as parts of Asia and Africa. Augustus also reorganized Rome's government and economy. His leadership brought great wealth—and a long period of peace—to the Roman world.

### VOCABULARY

**provinces** territories or districts

**restored** brought back to a normal, or usual, condition

**envoys** official messengers

**decree** an order or a command

*As you read, note how Augustus considers his wars and battles acts of justice rather than conquests for power and greed.*

I restored peace to the sea from pirates. In that slave war I handed over to their masters for the infliction of punishments about 30,000 captured, who had fled their masters and taken up arms against the state. All Italy swore allegiance to me voluntarily, and demanded me as leader of the war, which I won at Actium; the **provinces** of Gaul, Spain, Africa, Sicily, and Sardinia swore the same allegiance . . .

I extended the borders of all the provinces of the Roman people, which neighbored nations not subject to our rule. I **restored** peace to the provinces of Gaul and Spain, likewise Germany . . . I brought peace to the Alps from the region, which is near the Adriatic Sea to the Tuscan, with no unjust war waged against any nation. I sailed my ships on the ocean from the mouth of the Rhine to the east region up to the borders of the Cimbri, where no Roman had gone before that time by land or sea, and the Cimbri and the Charydes and the

From *The Deeds of the Divine Augustus* by Augustus, translated by Thomas Bushnell. Published by The Internet Classics Archive, 1998.

**The Deeds of the Divine Augustus,** *continued*       Primary Source

Semnones and the other Germans of the same
territory sought by **envoys** the friendship of me and
of the Roman people . . .

I added Egypt to the rule of the Roman people.
When Artaxes, king of Greater Armenia, was killed,
though I could have made it a province, I preferred,
by the example of our elders, to hand over that
kingdom to Tigranes, son of king Artavasdes . . .

I founded colonies of soldiers in Africa, Sicily,
Macedonia, each Spain, Greece, Asia, Syria,
Narbonian Gaul, and Pisidia, and furthermore had
twenty-eight colonies founded in Italy under my
authority, which were very populous and crowded
while I lived . . .

And for this merit of mine, by a senate **decree**, I
was called Augustus . . .

## WHAT DID YOU LEARN?

**1.** What were some of the lands that Augustus added to the Roman Empire?

_____

_____

**2.** Why would the Roman Senate by decree call this emperor "Augustus"?

_____

_____

**3.** If Augustus were alive today, do you think he would be considered a humanitarian
(a person devoted to helping others) or a dictator (someone who rules by force)?
Use examples from the passage to support your response.

_____

_____

_____

_____

**Early History of Europe**        Geography and History

# Rome's Trade Routes,

## First Century AD

As Rome expanded its network of roads, trade within the Roman Empire—and between other empires—became easier. But explorers and traders continued to sail the seas, seeking treasures from the great empires of the day.

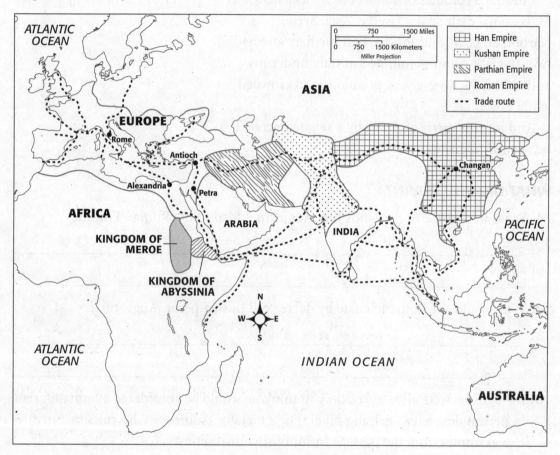

## MAP ACTIVITY

**1.** Use a red pencil or marker to shade the Roman Empire.

**2.** Use a blue pencil or marker to shade the Parthian Empire.

**3.** Use a yellow pencil or marker to shade the Kushan Empire.

**4.** Use a green pencil or marker to shade the Han Empire of China.

**5.** Use a black pencil or marker to show how traders traveled by road. Use an orange pencil or marker to show how traders traveled by sea.

Rome's Trade Routes, First Century AD, *continued*        Geography and History

## ANALYZING MAPS

1. **Movement**  Draw a line that shows the best route a trader in Antioch might
   take to buy pepper in India. Explain why the route you chose is the best route
   for the trader.

   _____

   _____

2. **Human/Environment Interaction**  Imagine you're a trader in the Roman Empire.
   Draw one trade route by road and one trade route by sea to Antioch. Which route
   do you think would be easier? Why?

   _____

   _____

3. **Region**  Most of the trade routes (whether by land or sea) don't take a very direct,
   point-to-point route. Explain why.

   _____

   _____

4. **Human/Environment Interaction**  What problems might you encounter if you
   traveled the trade routes marked on the map?

   _____

   _____

5. **Draw a Conclusion**  How might learning about different regions and their
   weather patterns affect trade?

   _____

   _____

**Early History of Europe**

# Social Studies Skills
## Geography

# Interpreting a Historical Map

## LEARN THE SKILL

Historical maps are not old documents made a long time ago—that would be a "historic map." Historical maps are current documents made to illustrate a place at a certain time in the past. A historical map may also explain some past event, such as a war or a plague. Historical maps help readers learn about the place or event by using different colors and symbols to represent information. For instance, arrows may show the path of a war. Keys are very important parts of historical maps. A reader can look at the key to see what the colors and symbols represent on the map.

## PRACTICE THE SKILL

Refer to the historical map of The First Crusade, 1096, in Section 3 of this chapter in your textbook. Interpret the map to answer the following questions.

1. In what direction would you be traveling if you traveled from Vienna to Jerusalem?

   _____

2. What years do the arrows represent on the map?

   _____

3. About how many miles separate Constantinople and Antioch?

   _____

4. Rome is on the coast of which sea?

   _____

5. In what country is Lyon located?

   _____

## APPLY THE SKILL

Refer to the historical map of Alexander the Great's Empire, c. 323 BC, in Section 1 of this chapter in your textbook. Write five questions about the map. Exchange questions with a partner and answer them. Remember, your questions should be based just on information from the map itself.

**Early History of Europe**               Geography for Life

# Transportation in Europe: Then and Now

## DANGER AHEAD! TRAVEL IN THE ANCIENT WORLD

Getting around ancient Europe took a lot of time and effort. The main
form of transportation on land was walking. People also rode horses or
used horses to pull carts or wagons. In ancient Rome, the rich would
sometimes force slaves to carry them—even for long distances.

However, for ancient Greeks and Romans, sea travel was essential to
their cultures and economies. For ancient Greeks, land travel was
difficult because of the geography of Greece. With many steep
mountains cutting off peninsulas, travel by boat was often more
efficient. For ancient Romans, with many miles of coastlines, their
geography also made the sea a ready source of transportation.

Whether by land or sea, travel in the ancient world was dangerous—
often a matter of life or death! Bandits often attacked travelers on the
roads, unless they had soldiers or private guards for protection. When
people needed to rest for the night, inns were few and far between.
Often thieves lurked about these inns, not to mention bed lice and
other bedbugs. Yet sea travel was not easy either. Ancient sailors
feared storms, pirates, and sea monsters (real and imagined).

## STALLED! TRAVEL DURING THE MIDDLE AGES

Transportation during the early Middle Ages declined in some ways.
People rarely ventured far from home. Roads were not kept in repair.
Europeans did make some strides in improving how they got around
their world. One such improvement was a better horse collar and shaft
for pulling. Although this may not seem significant to us today, a new
collar allowed horses to pull loads faster. Greater improvements resulted
from the Crusades. Europeans learned of new transportation
technology from their contact with the Muslims.

At sea, a fierce force rowed and sailed from what are now the
northern European countries of Denmark, Sweden, and Norway. The
Vikings, who were excellent shipbuilders and mariners, raided many
areas of Europe for about 250 years until around AD 1000. They were
ruthless raiders, but they also spread positive aspects of their culture
through much of Europe. During the later Middle Ages, Europeans
developed new types of sails, shipbuilding techniques, and navigational
aids. These advances helped lead the way for the age of exploration.
Compared to today, travel was still slow and dangerous, but improving.

## GO, GO, GO! TRAVEL IN EUROPE TODAY

Many centuries later, Europeans and their visitors have many more
options for transportation. A trip that may have taken early Europeans
weeks—even months—to travel may now take only a few hours. Some
of the "new" ways of getting around today include: high-speed (bullet)
trains, airplanes, cars, bikes, ferries, motorcycles, subways, buses, and
helicopters. You could even add rollerblades and skateboards to the list!

Like their ancestors, many European city-dwellers today still walk to
get around the city. However, many take public transportation, such as
buses or subways. Others drive motorized scooters or cars. Compared to
earlier times, travel is much more advanced. In general, it is also much
safer and faster. However, modern transportation still faces threats—
from terrorism and increasing fuel costs.

Who knows what travel will be like centuries from now?

## YOU ARE THE GEOGRAPHER

**1.** Compare and contrast travel in ancient Europe with travel today.

_____

_____

_____

_____

**2.** How did the Crusades lead to improvements in travel in Europe?

_____

_____

_____

_____

_____

**3.** A high-speed train trip from Milan, Italy, to Paris, France—a distance of about
500 miles—takes about seven hours. A person can walk about four miles an hour.
If you had to walk from Milan to Paris (as people did long ago) how many hours
would it take you without stopping? If you could only walk eight hours per day,
how many days would it take you? Explain whether you would rather travel by
train or by foot.

_____

_____

_____

**4.** Suppose you are a trader in ancient Rome or ancient Athens. How would you
travel to a distant city to trade your goods for others? Explain why you would
choose this method of transportation.

_____

_____

_____

**5.** Imagine you are a business owner of the future—in the year 2200—in Munich,
Germany. Describe a trip you might take for a business meeting in Madrid, Spain.
What problems might you encounter on your journey?

_____

_____

_____

# The Roads of Ancient Rome

*Stretching from the British Isles in the northwest to the Red Sea in the southeast, the Romans built the largest empire of the ancient world. To hold their empire together, the Romans constructed some 50,000 miles of roads in a remarkable feat of engineering for the times. To learn about ancient Roman roads and how they were constructed, study the information and complete the activities that follow.*

The ancient saying that "all roads lead to Rome" recognized not only the empire's geography, but also Rome's position as its political, military, and commercial "center." To symbolize Roman power, around the beginning of the Christian Era, Emperor Caesar Augustus had a huge map of the road system carved in marble and erected near the Senate building in the center of Rome. There it became a valuable source of information about the empire. Scribes made parchment copies of it for Roman generals and travelers, creating history's first road maps in the process.

**Roads of the Roman Empire**

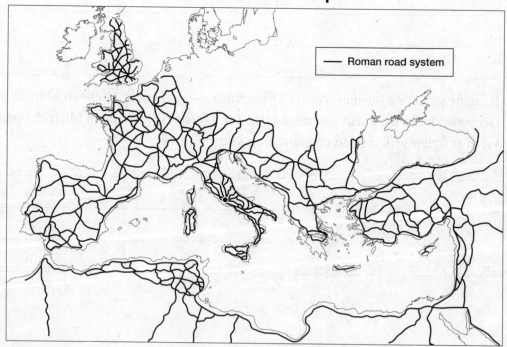

1. Use an atlas to help determine the shortest route a general would have followed to move legions from Rome to reinforce the Roman fort at Lutetia (now Paris) in the imperial province of Gallia. Mark out the route on the map.

2. Mark on the map the route a merchant from Antiochia (Antioch) would have followed to trade with the village of Aquincum (now Budapest).

## BUILDING THE ROAD

After the road's path was staked out, a worker used a plow to loosen
the soil and mark the trench margins, or <u>fossa</u>. Other workers then dug
a trench 6 to 9 feet deep and 9 to 12 feet wide for the road bed. After
the dirt at the bottom of the trench was pounded down to a firm bed,
a foundation of <u>pavimentum</u>—lime mortar or sand—was laid to form
a level base. Next came <u>statument</u>, which consisted of rocks about four
to five inches in diameter held together with mortar or clay. This layer
could be from 10 inches to 2 feet thick. On top of the statument,
workers poured <u>rudus</u>—9 to 12 inches of concrete filled with broken
pieces of pottery or stones. Atop this came the <u>nucleus</u>, a concrete
made of gravel or sand and lime. It was poured in layers, with each
layer compacted with a roller. The nucleus was rolled to a thickness of
one foot at the sides and 18 inches in the middle. This concave shape
allowed water to run off the road's surface. The top layer was the
<u>summum dorsum</u>, large blocks of stone that were 6 or more inches
thick. These were fitted on top of the still-moist nucleus. When the
road became worn, this top layer was removed and the blocks were
turned over or replaced.

**3.** Using the description above as a guide, label the diagram of a Roman road
in the making.

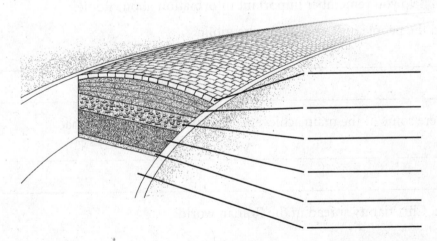

**4.** Why would Roman rulers have preferred expensive paved roads over cheaper dirt
ones in their efforts to control their empire?

_____

_____

**Early History of Europe**

# Focus on Reading

# Re-reading

Many readers do not fully understand what they read at first.
Re-reading is a strategy you can use to better understand a text passage.
After you read something the first time, ask yourself questions about
the reading. If you can't answer your own questions, re-read the passage
carefully. As you re-read, look for answers to your questions. So, if you
are ever not sure you fully understand what you have just read, be sure
to re-read it!

## SECTION 1: ANCIENT GREECE

Many historians consider ancient Greece the birthplace of modern
civilization. Re-read Section 1. Re-read carefully, looking for examples
of Greece's many contributions to the world. List one or two examples
of Greece's contributions in the following areas.

- architecture
- art
- government
- literature
- philosophy
- science

## SECTION 2: THE ROMAN WORLD

There are many key terms, places, and people mentioned in Section 2.
Re-read the section to help you answer the questions below. Your
answers will help you remember important information about Rome.

**1.** Why did the people of Rome create a republic?

_____

_____

**2.** What were some of the main achievements during the Pax Romana?

_____

_____

**3.** How did Christianity spread in the Roman world?

_____

_____

**4.** What were the main causes of the decline of Rome?

_____

_____

## SECTION 3: THE MIDDLE AGES

There are two main systems that controlled life in Europe in the Middle
Ages—the feudal system and the manor system. Write down the main
ideas you recall about each system from your first reading of "Life in
the Middle Ages" in Section 3. Then re-read the passage and add anything else you noticed from your second reading.

**The feudal system—first reading:** _____

_____

_____

**The feudal system—second reading:** _____

_____

_____

**The manor system—first reading:** _____

_____

_____

**The manor system—second reading:** _____

_____

_____

## FINDING ANSWERS TO YOUR QUESTIONS

Are there any parts of the "Early History of Europe" chapter that you
are still not sure you understood fully? Write down one question you
have for each section on the lines below. Then re-read the sections to
find the answers. Write the answers on the lines provided.

**My question for Section 1:** _____

**Answer:** _____

**My question for Section 2:** _____

**Answer:** _____

**My question for Section 3:** _____

**Answer:** _____

**Early History of Europe**

# Focus on Writing

## Writing a Myth

A myth is a story that tries to explain a natural or historical event. Your first task is to write a myth about an event from ancient and medieval Europe. Be sure to write your myth the way that people of this time might have written it. Follow the steps below to write your myth.

### PREWRITING

1. **Choosing Characters** On a separate piece of paper, list the people of ancient Greece you learned about in Section 1. As you read Sections 2 and 3, add more people to your list.

2. **Finding a Setting** Review Sections 1 and 2 for examples of possible settings for your myth. List these on a separate piece of paper. As you read Section 3, add possible settings from the Middle Ages to your list.

3. **Selecting a Topic** Review the entire chapter, looking for events that are most interesting to you. List these on a separate piece of paper.

4. **Finalizing Your Choices** Look over your lists of characters, setting, and topics. Which ones do you want to use for your myth? Write your final choices on the chart below.

---

**My Myth about the Early History of Europe**

My character(s) will be: _____

My setting will be: _____

My topic will be:_____

---

### WRITING

5. **Writing Your Myth** Use the information from your prewriting and the model on the next page to write your myth. (Use a separate piece of paper if you need more room.) Remember, you are trying to explain the event in a way that people of the time might have explained it.

- Write a title and an introduction for your myth.

- In your body paragraphs, tell the story that explains the event you chose. Include descriptive details so your myth comes alive.

- Write a conclusion that sums up the importance of your myth.

**Europe and Russia**

Title:_____

**Introduction:** _____

_____

_____

**Body:** _____

_____

_____

_____

_____

_____

**Conclusion:**_____

_____

_____

_____

## EVALUATING AND PROOFREADING

**6. Evaluating Your Myth** Does your myth describe an event from ancient and medieval Europe? Use the following questions to evaluate and revise your myth.

- Does your myth have an introduction, body, and conclusion?

- Did you use vivid, descriptive details?

- Is your myth written in the style of someone living in that time period?

- Did you proofread your myth for capitalization, spelling, and grammar errors?

**7. Proofreading Your Myth** Before you present your myth, check for correct punctuation, grammar, capitalization, and spelling.

Name _____ Class _____ Date _____

# Early History of Europe                     Chapter Review

**BIG IDEAS**

1. Through colonization, trade, and conquest, the Greeks spread their culture in Europe and Asia.
2. The Romans unified parts of Europe, Africa, and Asia in one of the ancient world's greatest civilizations.
3. Christianity and social systems influenced life in Europe in the Middle Ages.

## REVIEWING VOCABULARY, TERMS, AND PLACES

Using the clues provided, fill in the letter blanks with the correct term.

**1.** political units made up of a city and all the surrounding lands

— — — — - — — — — — —

**2.** channels used to carry water over long distances

— — — — — — — — — —

**3.** the head of the Christian church

— — — —

**4.** a large estate owned by a noble or a knight

— — — — —

**5.** a time in a society's history marked by great achievements

— — — — — — — — — — —

**6.** to make easier

— — — — — — — — — — —

**7.** greek-like, or the blended cultures of the Greeks and other people

— — — — — — — — — — —

**8.** a land that includes many different people under one rule

— — — — — — —

**9.** the region where Jesus lived

— — — — — — — —

Europe and Russia

**10.** another term for the medieval period

— — — — — —   — — — —

## COMPREHENSION AND CRITICAL THINKING

Read the **FALSE** statement below. On the line provided, replace the underlined word or words to make this statement **TRUE**.

**1.** The people of Rome created a new type of government called a/an <u>empire</u>.

_____

**2.** Alexander the Great was from an area called <u>Sparta</u>.

_____

**3.** A teenage girl named Joan of Arc was one of the most famous <u>philosophers and scholars</u> in all of European history.

_____

## REVIEWING THEMES

Answer the questions on the lines provided.

**1.** In which geography theme does the Parthenon fit: location, human-environment interaction, or place? Why?

_____

_____

**2.** Give three examples of "movement" in the early history of Europe.

_____

_____

## REVIEW ACTIVITY: ADVERTISEMENT

On a large piece of paper or poster board, create an advertisement for one of Europe's historic cities. Your advertisement should focus on the history of the city before 1500 as being the reason why a person should visit that city. You may want to choose one of these three cities:

Athens                    Rome                    London

Be sure to make your poster neat and attractive. Use bright colors, pictures, and words. Include at least six facts from the chapter when writing your ad.

# Research Project: The Black Death

## OVERVIEW/PURPOSE
Students will work in groups to research different aspects of the Black Death. Each group will present what they've learned to the rest of the class.

## PLANNING
### Time Suggested
Three 45-minute blocks and one week of outside class time for research

### Materials
- large paper or construction paper
- colored pencils, crayons, or paints and paintbrushes, scissors, glue or tape
- computer (with Internet access) and printer, or lined paper and pen
- Student Handout 1: Assignment A; "The Black Death Basics"
- Student Handout 2: Assignment B; "Battling the Black Death"
- Student Handout 3: Assignment C; "The Black Death's Path"
- Rubric: "Standards for Evaluating Your Work"

### Resources
http://go.hrw.com
http://www.bbc.co.uk/history/society_culture/welfare/black_01.shtml
*In the Wake of the Plague: The Black Death and the World It Made* © 2001 by Norman F. Cantor (The Free Press, NY).

### Preparation
- Schedule library time for research.

### Group Size
Students will break into small groups of 3–5.

## OBJECTIVES
- Research various aspects of the Black Death.
- Examine the historical context of the Black Death.
- Identify the health and medical factors of the Black Death.
- Create a presentation on the Black Death, including visuals.
- Work successfully in small groups.

## PROCEDURE

1. Define *plague (a contagious bacterial disease, or more generally an epidemic)* and brainstorm with students some reasons why people may be susceptible. Some examples may include lack of proper nutrition, lack of medicine, unsanitary living conditions, or travelers returning from foreign lands with new or rare diseases.

2. Explain that the Black Death was a series of deadly plagues that hit Europe in the mid-fourteenth century, killing millions.

3. Organize students into small groups and assign each group one of the following aspects of the Black Death to research (or allow groups to choose on their own):

   **a.** Assignment A—create a newspaper or magazine on the Black Death. Articles should explain the "Who, What, Where, When, How, and Why" of various aspects of the plague, such as its effects on daily life.

   **b.** Assignment B—create a TV report or documentary on the different medicines, treatments, and other methods used to try to stop the Black Death.

   **c.** Assignment C—create a historical map (or series of maps) to show where the Black Death started and spread, along with reasons why it spread as it did.

4. Distribute copies of **Handout 1: Black Death Basics** to groups doing assignment A. Distribute copies of **Handout 2: Battling the Black Death** to groups doing assignment B. Distribute copies of **Handout 3: The Black Death's Path** to groups doing assignment C. Distribute copies of **Rubric: Standards for Evaluating Your Work** to every student. Review the handouts with each group and respond to any questions they may have.

5. Provide students access to the Internet and/or library resources. Ask the librarian to set aside books and journal articles about the Black Death, plagues in general, the Middle Ages, medieval Europe, and historical maps.

6. Allow students time to complete the project outside of class as needed.

7. Plan class time for students to make their presentations and offer feedback.

## EXTEND

After the presentations, brainstorm with students about all the ways the Black Death affected society: in terms of its effects on the economy, art, politics, religion, and travel. Write the list on the board or on a chart. Ask the class to discuss whether a modern-day plague or epidemic would have the same effects. Why or why not? Some students may want to research other plagues or epidemics, such as the influenza (flu) epidemic of 1918.

**Early History of Europe**

Interdisciplinary Project

**Research Project: The Black Death**

## Assignment A: The Black Death Basics

### WHAT IS A PLAGUE?

In general, a plague is a disease that spreads rapidly and has a high death rate. Plague is actually caused by bacteria, or tiny germs. Rodents, such as rats, carry plague. It is spread to humans by fleas living on these rats. When the fleas bite people, they infect people with the plague bacteria. Unfortunately, fleas were very common in the Middle Ages.

### ASSIGNMENT A: RESEARCH PROJECT PLANNING GUIDE

Your research assignment is to find out the "who, what, where, when, why, and how" of the Black Death. Each person will conduct research to gather information about these aspects of the Black Death. Then your group will organize the information and plan a newspaper or magazine about the Black Death. You will each write an article, as well as edit and proofread other articles. You may also want to include appropriate visuals (such as drawings of scenes from the time) along with captions. Then present your newspaper or magazine to your class.

### PROJECT REQUIREMENTS

Your group's newspaper or magazine should provide the following information about the Black Death Basics in Europe:

- **Who** was affected by it?

- **What** was it like to experience it and to live in these times?

- **Where** did the Black Death occur? Which places were most affected by it?

- **When** did the Black Death affect Europe? How long afterward were its effects felt?

- **How** did people try to stop the plague? How were people's lives changed?

- **Why** did the plague affect so many people? Why did people react to it the way they did?

Include a project summary sheet that lists the names of the students in your group and gives a description of what each person contributed to your project.

**Early History of Europe**

# Interdisciplinary Project

## Research Project: The Black Death

# Assignment B: Battling the Black Death

## WHAT PROBLEMS DID PEOPLE FACE IN COPING WITH BLACK DEATH?

People's understanding of disease was very limited in the fourteenth century. Some problems may have been the following:

- The source of the plague was unknown.
- How the plague was spread was unknown.
- There was little or no medicine.
- The plague spread very quickly.
- A large number of people were dying.

## ASSIGNMENT B: RESEARCH PROJECT PLANNING GUIDE

Your research assignment is to list and explain the various medicines, treatments, and other methods used to try to stop the Black Death. Each person will conduct research to gather information. Then your group will organize the information and plan a TV report or documentary on your findings. Each person will write part of the script, as well as edit and proofread other parts of the script. You may also want to include some appropriate visuals (such as charts or diagrams) to support what the speaker is saying. Then present your TV report or documentary to your class. Plan to keep the total time of your report or documentary between 10–15 minutes.

## PROJECT REQUIREMENTS

Your group's presentation should provide the following information about Battling the Black Death in Europe:

- What types of medicines were used? What types of treatments were used? What other methods were used?
- How effective was each method at preventing or curing the Black Death?
- Which places, if any, kept their death toll low because they used more effective methods? Explain why these methods helped.
- Are any of the medicines, treatments, or other methods used in the past still used today? Is plague still a health risk? Explain why or why not.

Include a project summary sheet that lists each student's name and gives a description of what each person contributed to your project.

Europe and Russia

**Early History of Europe**  Interdisciplinary Project

# Assignment C: The Black Death's Path

## WHY DID THE BLACK DEATH SPREAD THE WAY IT DID?

Consider some of the possible reasons why the plague spread so fast and affected so many people in Europe. Possible reasons may include the following:

- overcrowding
- poor sanitation
- too many rats and fleas—and no pest control
- problems dealing with thousands of dead bodies

## ASSIGNMENT C: RESEARCH PROJECT PLANNING GUIDE

Your research assignment is to find out the Black Death's path in Europe from 1347 to 1351—and why it spread as it did. Each person will conduct research to gather information. Then your group will plan a historical map (or series of maps) to explain the Black Death's spread. You will create the map together, as well as edit and proofread it. Remember to use a key to explain the colors and symbols that represent information on your map. You will each also have to contribute to the writing of a brief explanation of why the plague spread as it did. Then present your map and explanation to your class.

## PROJECT REQUIREMENTS

Your group's presentation should provide the following information about the Black Death's Path in Europe:

- Your map shows where the Black Death struck in Europe—and when—and shows where it spread.

- It includes a key that explains what the map's colors and symbols represent. It includes the names of countries and major cities.

- If possible, it includes the number of deaths in each country (or city) as a result of the plague.

- Your explanation uses details to support your understanding of why the Black Death spread the way it did.

Include a project summary sheet that lists each student's name and gives a description of what each person contributed to your project.

**Early History of Europe**          Interdisciplinary Project

**Research Project: The Black Death**

# Standards for Evaluating Your Work

**EXCELLENT**

- The presentation includes all required information.

- The presentation is well researched and well presented.

- The visuals are well organized, visually pleasing, and well made.

- The project includes a summary sheet, showing how all members of the group contributed to the project.

**GOOD**

- The presentation includes most of the required information.

- The presentation shows good research and is clearly presented.

- The visuals are organized, neat, and adequately made.

- The project includes a summary sheet, showing how most members of the group contributed to the project.

**ACCEPTABLE**

- The presentation includes some of the required information.

- The presentation shows some research and is reasonably presented but needs more supporting facts and editing.

- The visuals are somewhat organized and fairly well made.

- The project includes a summary sheet, showing how some members of the group contributed to the project.

**UNACCEPTABLE**

- The presentation is missing significant amounts of required information.

- The presentation is poorly researched, poorly presented, and contains factual errors or lacks supporting details.

- The visuals are poorly organized or not well made.

- The project does not include a summary sheet, or the summary sheet shows how only a few members of the group contributed to the project.

**History of Early Modern Europe**  Vocabulary Builder

| | | |
|---|---|---|
| Catholic Reformation | Florence | humanism |
| perspective | Protestants | Reformation |
| Renaissance | Venice | Wittenberg |

**DIRECTIONS** On the line provided before each statement, write **T** if a statement is true and **F** if a statement is false. If the statement is false, write the term from the word bank that would make the statement correct on the line after each sentence.

_____ **1.** Lasting from about 1350 to 1500, the <u>Reformation</u> was a period of great creativity in Europe.

_____

_____ **2.** People who followed Martin Luther in forming their own religion became the first <u>Protestants</u>.

_____

_____ **3.** The technique of <u>humanism</u> enabled artists to show a realistic three-dimensional scene on a flat surface.

_____

_____ **4.** Italian cities such as Florence and <u>Wittenberg</u> became rich through trade.

_____

_____ **5.** <u>Catholic Reformation</u> emphasized the abilities and accomplishments of human beings.

_____

**DIRECTIONS** Choose five of the vocabulary words from the word bank. On a separate sheet of paper, use these words to write a story or poem that relates to the section.

# History of Early Modern Europe

## Vocabulary Builder

### Section 2

| | | |
|---|---|---|
| astrolabe | caravel | Christopher Columbus |
| circumnavigate | Galileo | gravity |
| New World | Queen Isabella | Scientific Revolution |
| Sir Isaac Newton | Vasco da Gama | |

**DIRECTIONS** Read each sentence and fill in the blank with the word in the word pair that best completes the sentence

1. In 1632 _____ was arrested for writing that Earth orbited the sun. (**Sir Isaac Newton/Galileo**)

2. The _____ led to the birth of modern science. (**Scientific Revolution/astrolabe**)

3. Without the support of _____, the voyage of Columbus might not have taken place. (**Queen Isabella/Sir Isaac Newton**)

4. In 1498 _____ sailed around the southern tip of Africa and on to India. (**Chrisopher Columbus/Vasco da Gama**)

5. _____ made important observations about the force of gravity. (**Sir Isaac Newton/Galileo**)

**DIRECTIONS** Write a word or phrase that has the same meaning as the term given.

6. New World _____

7. circumnavigate _____

8. astrolabe _____

9. logical _____

10. gravity _____

Europe and Russia

**History of Early Modern Europe**　　　Vocabulary Builder

| | |
|---|---|
| Bastille | Declaration of Independence |
| English Bill of Rights | Enlightenment |
| Napoleon Bonaparte | Reign of Terror |
| Declaration of the Rights of Man and of the Citizen | |

**DIRECTIONS** Answer each question by writing a sentence that contains at least one term from the word bank.

**1.** How did England's Parliament limit the monarchy's power?

_____

_____

_____

**2.** What peaceful steps did France take to guarantee its people more freedoms?

_____

_____

_____

**3.** What effect did Enlightenment ideas have on the British colonies in North America?

_____

_____

_____

**4.** What period came right after the French Revolution? Why was it called this?

_____

_____

_____

**5.** What event took place after Napoleon's defeat in 1814? What was its result?

_____

_____

_____

# History of Early Modern Europe

# Vocabulary Builder

## Section 4

| | | |
|---|---|---|
| capitalism | Industrial Revolution | inventions |
| invest | steam power | suffragette |
| technology | textiles | |

**DIRECTIONS** Look at each set of four terms following each number. On the line provided, write the letter of the term that does not relate to the others.

_____ **1. a.** voting     **b.** suffragette     **c.** guillotine     **d.** women

_____ **2. a.** Jethro Tull     **b.** textiles     **c.** cloth     **d.** factories

_____ **3. a.** capitalism     **b.** profit     **c.** investment     **d.** military

_____ **4. a.** inventions     **b.** machines     **c.** literature     **d.** technology

_____ **5. a.** steam power     **b.** iron     **c.** profit     **d.** steel

**DIRECTIONS** Write three words or phrases that describe each term.

**6.** capitalism _____

**7.** textiles _____

**8.** suffragette _____

**9.** Industrial Revolution _____

**10.** technology _____

**History of Early Modern Europe**

# Biography

# Galileo
c. 1564–1642

 **HOW HE AFFECTED THE WORLD** Galileo is remembered as one of the world's greatest scientists. He is known as the father of modern **astronomy.** He is also known for his work in **physics,** mathematics, and philosophy

 *As you read the biography below,* think about how Galileo's work helped pave the way for other great scientists and thinkers.

As a young man, Galileo studied medicine and philosophy at the University of Pisa in Italy. Although his father wanted him to become a doctor, Galileo was more interested in math. After four years, he left the university without getting a degree. He taught privately for a few years, then he took a teaching position at his old university.

Galileo was a brilliant man with many ideas about physics and motion. Some of his ideas went against the beliefs of his time, many of which had been developed by the ancient Greek philosopher Aristotle. Galileo's ideas began to spread across Europe.

In 1609 Galileo heard about an invention that allowed far away objects to be seen as if they were nearby. He quickly reproduced this invention—an early telescope. Then he greatly improved upon it. He built an even more powerful telescope and used it to observe the night sky. With his more advanced telescopes, Galileo began closely observing the moon. He discovered that the moon's surface was rough and uneven, not smooth as many had thought. Galileo made many other discoveries about the planets and space.

**VOCABULARY**

**astronomy** study of planets and stars in outer space

**physics** the science of matter and energy, and how they relate

Galileo, *continued*                          Biography

Galileo's observations led him to believe that Earth revolved around the sun. This was very controversial at the time. At that time church leaders believed that the sun and planets revolved around Earth. Galileo wrote a book about his findings in 1632. After church leaders read his work, he was called to Rome to face the Inquisition. This was a group of church leaders who brought to trial anyone who went against the church's beliefs.

At first, Galileo would not take back what he had claimed. But later he gave in. He said that he had made a mistake by publishing his book. Some claim that he did so because he was threatened with torture and death. Galileo was forced to spend the rest of his life under house arrest. As he grew older, Galileo became blind. Still, he continued his scientific experiments—working right up until his death.

Galileo believed in using science to learn about the world. His discoveries would forever change how people viewed themselves and the universe.

## WHAT DID YOU LEARN?

**1. Recall** How did Galileo discover that the Earth revolved around the sun?

_____

_____

**2. Expressing and Supporting a Point of View** Why do you think Galileo was known as the father of modern astronomy?

_____

_____

## ACTIVITY

Imagine that you have been asked to interview Galileo for a newspaper. What would you want to ask him? Think of at least three questions. Write down your questions, then work with a partner to brainstorm what Galileo's answers might be.

**History of Early Modern Europe**                    Biography

# Napoleon Bonaparte

c. 1769–1821

**HOW HE AFFECTED THE REGION**
Napoleon became emperor of France in 1804.
He is remembered for creating a new French
system of law. But he is most famous for his
military successes and failures

*As you read the biography below,* think about
how Napoleon's ambition helped him rise
to power.

Napoleon was born on the island of Corsica,
which had become part of France. Growing up, he
attended military school. He graduated from the
military academy in Paris when he was just 16 years
old. As a military leader, Napoleon took part in
many military **campaigns**. He also became involved
in politics.

In 1799 Napoleon was serving in Egypt. At
the time, after the French Revolution, France's
government was weak. An ambitious man,
Napoleon took advantage of the situation. He
returned to Paris with a small army and took over
France's government. Then Napoleon and his group
set up a new government. They wrote a new
constitution, giving Napoleon the position of First
Consul. He was now the most powerful person
in France.

Napoleon worked hard to **reform** the country
after the French Revolution. He made changes
to France's government, legal system, and tax
system. He created a system of public education,
including a university system. He reformed France's
banking system. In 1801 he successfully negotiated
an agreement with the Catholic Church. This helped

**VOCABULARY**
**campaigns** battles
**reform** improve, reorganize
**censored** concealed,
 covered up
**exiled** banished, sent away

restore religious peace to France. Napoleon also created a new set of laws, called the Napoleonic Code. The Code dealt with property rights and other legal issues. It would influence the laws of many other countries.

In 1804 Napoleon wanted more power, so he crowned himself emperor of France. As emperor, Napoleon was a harsh ruler. He brought back the use of noble titles. He **censored** the press. He also tried to expand France's empire across Europe through military campaigns.

Although some of these failed, Napoleon had many military successes. At the peak of his power, he ruled over much of Europe. However, he was soundly defeated in 1814 and again in 1815. Napoleon was then **exiled** to Saint Helena, a small island in the Atlantic Ocean, where he died in 1821.

Although known more for his military might, Napoleon's reforms had a lasting influence on France—and all of Europe.

## WHAT DID YOU LEARN?

1. **Recall** What were some of the things that Napoleon accomplished during his lifetime?

_____

_____

2. **Expressing and Supporting a Point of View** What do you think was Napoleon's greatest accomplishment? Provide reasons to support your point of view.

_____

_____

## ACTIVITY

As a military leader, Napoleon had many great successes and some important failures. Using the Internet or a library resource center, research his military career. Then create a time line showing key events in his rise to power and his final defeat.

# Frankenstein
## by Mary Wollstonecraft Shelley

**ABOUT THE READING** Written in 1816, but not published until 1818, *Frankenstein* blends science fiction with important social themes such as poverty and social class. In the novel, Victor Frankenstein is a scientist who tries to bring a dead body to life. Once he does, however, he is disgusted by what he has done. The excerpt below describes Frankenstein's reaction to his creature.

**VOCABULARY**

**convulsive** involuntary contraction

**catastrophe** disaster

**delineate** describe

**endeavoured** attempted, tried

**ardour** passion, strong feelings

***As you read the passage below,*** *pay attention to how Victor Frankenstein describes his creature—and what his description reveals about Frankenstein's feelings.*

It was already one in the morning; the rain pattered dismally against the panes, and my candle was nearly burnt out, when, by the glimmer of the half-extinguished light, I saw the dull yellow eye of the creature open; it breathed hard, and a **convulsive** motion agitated its limbs.

How can I describe my emotions at this **catastrophe**, or how **delineate** the wretch whom with such infinite pains and care I had **endeavoured** to form? His limbs were in proportion, and I had selected his features as beautiful. Beautiful! . . . His yellow skin scarcely covered the work of muscles and arteries beneath; his hair was of a lustrous black, and flowing; his teeth of a pearly whiteness; but these luxuriances only formed a more horrid contrast with his watery eyes, that seemed almost of the same colour as the dun-white sockets in which

> Frankenstein had worked very hard to bring a dead body to life. Why do you think he now calls his deed a catastrophe?
>
> _____
> _____
> _____

> Circle the words the character uses to describe the creature's physical features.

Source: from *Frankenstein* by Mary Wollstonecraft Shelley.
Online Source http://www.gutenberg.org

they were set, his shrivelled complexion and straight black lips.

The different accidents of life are not so changeable as the feelings of human nature. I had worked hard for nearly two years, for the sole purpose of infusing life into an inanimate body. For this I had deprived myself of rest and health. I had desired it with an **ardour** that far exceeded moderation; but now that I had finished, the beauty of the dream vanished, and breathless horror and disgust filled my heart. Unable to endure the aspect of the being I had created, I rushed out of the room and continued a long time traversing my bed-chamber, unable to compose my mind to sleep . . .

> **Frankenstein had not fully considered what could happen if he succeeded in creating life.**

## ANALYZING LITERATURE

**1. Main Idea** How does Frankenstein react when he first sees his creature brought to life?

_____

_____

**2. Critical Thinking: Drawing Inferences** Mary Shelley wrote this novel after the Industrial Revolution had started in England. How do you think she might have felt about the advancements in technology that were taking place?

_____

_____

**3. Critical Thinking: Making Predictions** Frankenstein is disgusted by his creature and tries to go to sleep to forget about it. What do you think will happen next?

_____

_____

## ACTIVITY

On a separate piece of paper, draw a picture of what you think Frankenstein's creature looks like. Use the descriptions in the excerpt to help you decide how to draw the creature.

**History of Early Modern Europe**  Primary Source

# The Notebooks of Leonardo da Vinci

**ABOUT THE READING** Widely regarded as a genius, Leonardo da Vinci was an Italian Renaissance painter and sculptor. His notebooks include text and drawings of many of his theories and inventions. He also writes about painting techniques, including perspective. In this selection da Vinci explains how artists must pay close attention to detail.

**VOCABULARY**

**infinite** endless, countless

**prolong** draw out, lengthen

**diligence** carefulness, thoroughness

*As you read,* focus on how da Vinci gives examples to help support his ideas.

**491.**

<u>WHAT RULES SHOULD BE GIVEN TO BOYS LEARNING TO PAINT.</u>

We know for certain that sight is one of the most rapid actions we can perform. In an instant we see an **infinite** number of forms, still we only take in thoroughly one object at a time. <u>Supposing that you, Reader, were to glance rapidly at the whole of this written page</u>, you would instantly perceive that it was covered with various letters; but you could not, in the time, recognise what the letters were, nor what they were meant to tell. Hence you would need to see them word by word, line by line to be able to understand the letters. Again, if you wish to go to the top of a building you must go up step by step; otherwise it will be impossible that you should reach the top. Thus I say to you, whom nature prompts to pursue this art, if you wish to have a sound knowledge of the forms of objects begin with the details of them, and do not go on to the second [step] till you have the first well fixed in memory

> During the Renaissance, painters, sculptors, and other artists were usually men.

> Notice how da Vinci addresses the reader directly. He wanted to publish a piece on painting, but never completed it.

Source: *The Notebooks of Leonardo da Vinci, Complete* translated by Jean Paul Richter. Online source http://www.gutenberg.org.

**The Notebooks of Leonardo da Vinci,** *continued*                    Primary Source

and in practice. And if you do otherwise you will throw away your time, or certainly greatly **prolong** your studies. And remember to acquire **diligence** rather than rapidity.

> Da Vinci wrote in Italian, his native language. He also used a unique style known as "mirror writing," which went from right to left.

## WHAT DID YOU LEARN?

**1.** What does da Vinci believe is necessary to understand the forms of objects, or how things look?

_____

_____

**2.** Do you think da Vinci's advice could also apply to other fields of study? Why or why not?

_____

_____

_____

# Magellan's Voyage around the World

Although born into a noble family in Portugal, Magellan won fame
while sailing for Spain. A dispute with the Portuguese king led Magellan
to seek support from Spain's King for a voyage across the Atlantic
Ocean—and around the world. Magellan was outfitted with five ships
and about 270 sailors. He set sail from Spain in 1519. When he reached
the tip of South America, he navigated through a channel, or strait.
It would later be called the Strait of Magellan in his honor. He then
sailed west into the Pacific Ocean, reaching the Philippines, where he
was killed. Only one of Magellan's ships—with only 18 sailors—made
it across the Pacific Ocean, around Africa, and home to Spain in 1522.
The first voyage around the world had finally been completed!

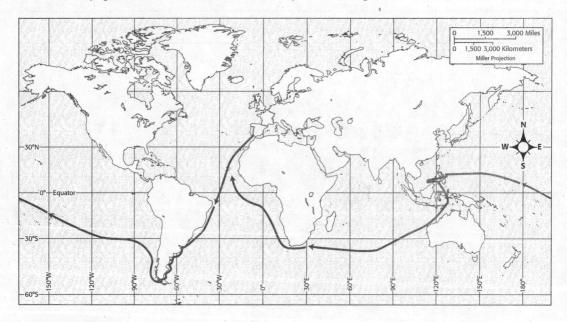

## MAP ACTIVITY

**1.** Label the following on the map: Spain, Europe, South America, Asia, Africa,
Atlantic Ocean, Pacific Ocean, Indian Ocean.

**2.** Use a bright color to highlight the continent of South America. Use another
bright color to highlight the continent of Asia. Use a third bright color to
highlight the continent of Africa.

**3.** Update the map legend to reflect the colors that you have added to the map.

## ANALYZING MAPS

**1. Location**  On what continent did Magellan first land during his voyage?

_____

_____

**2. Human/Environment Interaction**  What geographical feature first navigated by Magellan links the Atlantic and Pacific Oceans?

_____

_____

**3. Movement**  Upon what oceans did Magellan and his crew sail?

_____

_____

**4. Draw a Conclusion**  Why was Magellan's voyage so important?

_____

_____

**History of Early Modern Europe**          Social Studies Skills

# Making Economic Choices

## LEARN THE SKILL

Making economic choices involves sacrifices, or trade-offs. If you choose to spend your money on a movie, for example, the trade-offs are the other things you could have bought with the money. Most economic choices involve many trade-offs. The best alternative that you must give up when you make your final choice is called the trade-off.

## PRACTICE THE SKILL

Suppose you have earned $20 for babysitting. Your friend has asked you to go to the movies this weekend, which would cost $10. You have also had your eye on a new video game—on sale this week for $20. Finally, your parents have started a college fund for you. For every dollar you save, they will put in another dollar (so your $20 would be like saving $40). What will you do with your $20? What trade-offs are involved with each choice? Complete the chart below to evaluate your choices.

| Possible Choices | Benefits | Trade-offs |
|---|---|---|
| Go to movies ($10) | | |
| Buy video game ($20) | | |
| Save for college ($___) | | |

Write your final choice(s) here: _____

Write the trade-off here: _____

Explain why you made your final choice here: _____

_____

## APPLY THE SKILL

Create a chart like the one above to evaluate an economic choice you have to make. Write down the benefits and trade-offs for each possible choice. Then write down your final choice(s) and the trade-off associated with your decision. Explain why you made your final choice.

**History of Early Modern Europe**          Geography for Life

# Italian Renaissance Cities: A Modern Way of Life?

## MOVING FROM THE COUNTRY TO THE CITY

During the Middle Ages, most people lived as peasants in the country, farming on land that was owned by a king or feudal lord. Most peasants barely made enough to survive and pay their rent.

During the Renaissance, however, many Italian cities were thriving with commerce. Italian cities needed skilled workers and apprentices. Inventions like the printing press created new jobs, as did advances in shipbuilding and metallurgy. As a result, many peasants left the country and moved to the city. They sought new economic opportunities—and also to escape from burdensome debts to their lords.

## WORKING IN THE CITY

City workers tended to live in small areas within the city. There, men could practice a craft like woodworking, blacksmithing, or shoemaking. Women could weave cloth from linen, silk, or wool. Most craftspeople would run a small business out of their home—often just two rooms. Cities were walled-in, to protect the residents from bands of robbers or rival armies from other cities.

Professional guilds, like today's labor unions, were formed. These guilds helped the families of injured workers. They also protected guild members from unfair competition. They set quality standards for products and training standards for apprentices.

Kings and queens didn't rule over the cities of Renaissance Italy. Each city had its own government. Rulers were called princes, but many were from wealthy merchant families—not royal families. City governments were generally elected. Although in Florence, for example, where 100,000 people lived, only 3,200 men were eligible to vote.

Although banks were present during the Middle Ages, the church had strict rules against lending money for profit. However, due to the great increase in trade during the Renaissance, banking grew into a huge industry. It was still dangerous for merchants to carry large amount of money with them when they traveled. So bills of exchange—similar to the checks people use today—became accepted. These "checks" could then be cashed at banks throughout Renaissance Europe.

Outside of cities, the ideas of the Renaissance spread—as did word of new opportunities. Some peasants rebelled against their lords and kings.

They demanded better working agreements. Others continued the move to the city.

## CHANGES FOR MANY

The opportunity to better oneself through education became available to more people at this time. Although few city workers sent their children to school, public education was available to most in the Renaissance cities of Italy.

During the late Renaissance period, it also became more acceptable for women to become educated. Some women became successful in business as tailors, brewers, and silk manufacturers. Women wrote, painted, and even ruled countries. Louise of Savoy, Elizabeth of England and Isabella of Spain were three such rulers.

As more people grew wealthy, the demand for artists and architects grew. Viewed as common craft workers in earlier times, painters, sculptors, and architects were now seen as gifted geniuses. Even popes, princes, and other royalty looked up to them. For example, Michelangelo came from a wealthy family. They strongly discouraged him from becoming an artist because of its low status at the time. However, in his lifetime, artists such as Michelangelo earned large sums of money for their work. They became sought-after throughout all of Europe—and many would travel to work all over Europe.

Instead of being tied down to the land, Europeans were on the move!

## YOU ARE THE GEOGRAPHER

**1.** Compare and contrast city life in Renaissance Italy with city life today.

_____

_____

_____

_____

**2.** Why do you think peasants moved from the country to the city during the Renaissance? Give reasons to support your answer.

_____

_____

_____

_____

**3.** Do you think it is still common today for people in the country to move to the city? Why or why not?

_____

_____

_____

_____

**4.** Suppose you are living in Europe during the Renaissance. What job would you choose to do to earn a living? Where would you choose to live? Give reasons to support your answers.

_____

_____

_____

_____

**5.** If you lived in Italy during the Renaissance, what would a typical day be like for you? Describe your day using vivid details.

_____

_____

_____

_____

**History of Early Modern Europe**              Critical Thinking

# The Industrial Revolution:
# Two Viewpoints

### IT WAS A TIME OF GROWTH, WEALTH, AND PROGRESS

Bankers, investors, factory owners, land owners and inventors made
millions of dollars during the years of the Industrial Revolution.
Products could be made faster and cheaper. For example, consider
the cost of cloth. As a result of factory production, the cost of making
cotton yarn decreased by 90% and the cost of making woolen cloth
decreased by 50% by the mid 1800s. These innovations made products
more affordable for the average person. Hundreds of thousands of jobs
were created. Bridges, roads, and railroad tracks were built, improving
transportation for shipping and travel. These jobs offered an alternative
to the hard—and unpredictable—life of farming. They offered regular
wages for a growing population. Finally, wealthy industrialists also
donated large sums of money to good causes to help improve society.

### IT WAS A TIME OF MISERY AND INJUSTICE

Men, women, and children—some as young as 3—worked in dangerous,
noisy, and unhealthy factories. Their wages were low, and they
sometimes had to work 16-hour days. Work rooms could be filled
with dust or smoke. Machines had no safety equipment. Hair, fingers,
and arms could easily get caught in them. As a result, injuries and
death were common. Parliament, England's governing body, had a
laissez-faire, or no interference, policy toward industry. At this time,
only the wealthy were members of Parliament. It would hurt business
too much, they said, to set rules for health and safety or minimum
wages. When workers began to protest unfair working conditions,
Parliament created the Combination Acts (1799–1800). These acts made
it illegal for workers to even meet to talk about improving their working
conditions. Fortunately, by the late 1800s many reform acts were passed.
These reform acts finally helped to improve working conditions and
limit child labor.

1. Which viewpoint of the Industrial Revolution do you think is most accurate?
   Give reasons to support your answers.

   _____

   _____

   _____

**2.** What is a laissez-faire policy? Were the Combination Laws truly a laissez-faire policy? Why or why not?

_____

_____

_____

**3.** Imagine you are the owner of a factory during the Industrial Revolution. Describe what it would be like to work in your factory. Use vivid details.

_____

_____

_____

**4.** Would you buy a product if you knew that the workers who made it were working under unsafe or unfair conditions? Why or why not?

_____

_____

_____

**5.** What do you think our government can do ensure safe and fair conditions for workers in our country? What if the workers are in other countries?

_____

_____

_____

**History of Early Modern Europe**　　　Focus on Reading

# Understanding Chronological Order

*Chronological* means "related to time." Many of the events in this chapter are written about in sequence, or in the order in which they happened. Words such as *first, before, after, then, next,* and *later* often indicate the sequence events took place, or chronological order. One way to help remember and organize events in sequence is to put them in a time line.

## SETTING UP YOUR TIME LINE

On a large piece of paper or poster board, create a time line like the one below. Below the time line, write the name of the chapter.

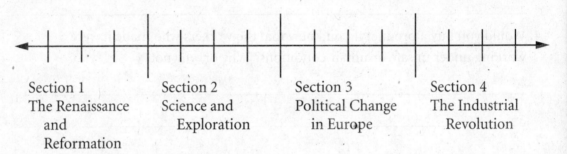

Section 1　　　　Section 2　　　　Section 3　　　　Section 4
The Renaissance　Science and　　Political Change　The Industrial
and　　　　　　　Exploration　　in Europe　　　Revolution
Reformation

## ADDING EVENTS TO YOUR TIME LINE

Review the chapter and your notes. On the time line, list major events in the order in which they took place. You should include important inventions and discoveries, voyages and expeditions, revolutions and military battles, and other key events from the chapter.

## EVALUATING

Does your time line accurately list the sequence of events for the four time periods in the chapter?

### Rubric

- Does your time line include important events from each section?
- Is the time line organized correctly, in order by date?
- Is your time line neatly done and attractive?
- Are there any spelling or grammatical mistakes?

**History of Early Modern Europe**                    Focus on Writing

# Creating a Travel Brochure

Your task is to persuade people to visit Europe—but a Europe of long
ago. Choose one of the periods from the Renaissance through the
Industrial Revolution. What would visitors to this time period
experience? What events might they witness? Who would they meet?
What ideas would they learn about? Describe everything that would
make a person want to visit this time period in your brochure.

## PREWRITING

1. **Choosing a Time Period**  Review the chapter and look back over your Focus on
   Writing notes. Choose a time period that most interests you for your brochure.
   Think about a title for your brochure such as "Visit the Renaissance: For Art
   Lovers!"

2. **Gathering Information**  Write down at least four topics to include in your
   brochure. For example, you could describe inventions and discoveries, interesting
   people, historical events, art and literature, and where people lived and worked.
   Be sure to include enough details to write vivid descriptions later.

3. **Gathering Images**  Look through magazines, books, and newspapers and browse
   the Internet to find images that relate to the time period you have chosen.
   Examples might include a painting by a famous Renaissance artist or a picture of
   a famous person or invention. You may even want to create images yourself, such
   as drawings on paper and computer graphics you print out.

4. **Reviewing Information**  Look over your notes. Which details do you want to
   emphasize in your brochure? Do you need to gather more information about any
   topic? Do you have several appropriate visuals?

5. **Organizing Your Brochure**  Make an outline from your notes to organize your
   brochure. Your brochure will have eight panels, so you need to fill each panel. You
   may want to have an image and description on each panel, or alternate between a
   description and an image for each panel. Think about how you can organize your
   brochure so it is very appealing to readers.

## WRITING

6. **Writing Descriptions**  Write at least one descriptive paragraph for each topic
   you have chosen. Use the information you gathered in your notes. Descriptions
   should be written in paragraph form. Each paragraph should be about four or
   five sentences in length and begin with a topic sentence, or main idea. Include
   two or three supporting detail sentences and end with a summary sentence.

To add more interest for your readers, write a headline for each topic, such as "Meet the Emperor of France," if you are writing about Napoleon. Write a caption to go with each image you choose.

Remember, your goal is to encourage people to visit the time period you have selected. Your writing should make this time in Europe come alive for your readers, so they are really excited about visiting it.

7. **Creating Your Brochure** Fold a piece of paper in half and then fold it in half again, so you have 8 panels. Make the first panel the cover for your brochure. Write the title on the cover. Include one or more images for your cover.

Then follow your outline, adding your descriptions and images so every panel is completed in the order you planned.

## EVALUATING AND PROOFREADING

8. **Evaluating Your Brochure** Does your brochure give an accurate and exciting representation of the time period you chose? Use the questions below to evaluate and revise your brochure.

### Rubric

- Is the information you included factual? Do the images support the information?
- Does each descriptive paragraph include a topic sentence? Does each descriptive paragraph include supporting details?
- Does your brochure encourage readers to visit this time period?

9. **Proofreading Your Brochure** To perfect your travel brochure before sharing it, check the following:

- Is the brochure neatly done and attractive?
- Are there any spelling or grammatical mistakes?
- Are all proper names and places capitalized?
- Did you use complete sentences?

## PRESENTING

10. **Presenting Your Travel Brochure** Here are two ways to present your brochure:

- Give a presentation by reading your brochure aloud. Remember to speak with enthusiasm and to make eye contact. Be sure to also show the images in your brochure so everyone can see them.
- Post your brochure for classmates to review on their own.

# History of Early Modern Europe

## Chapter Review

### BIG IDEAS

1. The periods of the Renaissance and the Reformation introduced new ideas and new ways of thinking into Europe.

2. New inventions and knowledge led to European exploration and empires around the world.

3. Ideas of the Enlightenment inspired revolutions and new governments in Europe.

4. Driven by new ideas and technologies, much of Europe developed industrial societies in the 1700s and 1800s.

## REVIEWING VOCABULARY, TERMS, AND PLACES

Use the description in the right column to unscramble the term or name in the box. Write the correct term or name in the space provided.

SSCERENANAI

1. _____ period of great creativity in art, literature, and science, which lasted from about 1350 to 1500

MAREIONFORT

2. _____ religious reform movement that began in Germany

VICIRTECUGAMNA

3. _____ to sail all the way around Earth

LEGALIO

4. _____ Italian scientist arrested for writing that Earth orbited the sun

NEMENIHTENTLG

5. _____ known as the Age of Reason, a period that placed great importance on logical thought

SMCAALIPIT

6. _____ a new economic system resulting from the Industrial Revolution

GESRATFTFUES

7. _____ women from Great Britain who campaigned for the right to vote

RCCONATT

8. _____ a binding legal agreement

## COMPREHENSION AND CRITICAL THINKING

Read each of the following pairs of sentences, and cross out the **FALSE** sentence.

**1. a.** People who followed Martin Luther in a split from the Catholic Church became the first humanists.

  **b.** People who followed Martin Luther in a split from the Catholic Church became the first Protestants.

**2. a.** During the Catholic Reformation, church leaders worked to make church teachings easier for people to understand.

  **b.** During the Catholic Reformation, church leaders worked to build political power.

**3. a.** Approved in 1689, the English Bill of Rights listed rights for Parliament and the English people.

  **b.** Approved in 1689, the Declaration of the Rights of Man and of the Citizen listed rights for Parliament and the English people.

**4. a.** Louis XVI crowned himself emperor of France in 1804 and created a new French legal system.

  **b.** Napoleon Bonaparte crowned himself emperor of France in 1804 and created a new French legal system.

**5. a.** The Industrial Revolution began in Great Britain.

  **b.** The Industrial Revolution began in Italy.

## REVIEWING THEMES

Using the lists below, determine what theme from geography they have in common.

**1.** _____        French Revolution, Congress of Vienna, Duomo Cathedral

**2.** _____        caravel, steam train, Strait of Magellan

**3.** _____        trade routes, exploration, water power

## REVIEW ACTIVITY: JOURNAL ENTRY

Imagine that you are a young person living in one of the four periods covered in this chapter: the Renaissance and Reformation, the Scientific Revolution, the Enlightenment, or the Industrial Revolution. Write a fictional journal entry that gives details about your life. Talk about where you live, the events that are happening around you, and your hopes for the future.

**Modern European History**                    Vocabulary Builder

**Section 1**

| | | | |
|---|---|---|---|
| alliance | Allies | Central Powers | communism |
| nationalism | stalemate | Treaty of Versailles | trench warfare |

**DIRECTIONS** Answer each question by writing a sentence that contains
at least one term from the word bank.

**1.** What led to the tension that sparked World War I?

_____

_____

**2.** What countries fought each other in World War I?

_____

_____

**3.** How did the new kind of fighting seen in World War I affect the soldiers?

_____

_____

**4.** What did the final peace settlement of World War I demand of Germany?

_____

_____

**5.** How did World War I change the way some European countries were governed?

_____

_____

**DIRECTIONS** Look up the vocabulary term *alliance* in the dictionary.
Write the dictionary definition of the word that is closest to the definition
used in your textbook.

_____

_____

_____

# Modern European History

# Vocabulary Builder

**Section 2**

| Allies | Axis Powers | dictator |
| Great Depression | Holocaust | Nazi |

**DIRECTIONS** On the line provided before each statement, write **T** if the statement is true and **F** if the statement is false. If the statement is false, write the term that makes the sentence a true statement on the line after each sentence.

_____ **1.** The two alliances fighting in World War II were the Allies and the <u>Nazi Powers</u>.

_____

_____ **2.** The <u>Great Depression</u> was triggered by the stock market crash in 1929.

_____

_____ **3.** Benito Mussolini was Italy's first <u>communist</u>.

_____

_____ **4.** During the Holocaust, the <u>Nazi</u> government tried to wipe out Europe's Jews.

_____

_____ **5.** Vladimir Lenin and <u>Joseph Stalin</u> were both communist leaders of the Soviet Union.

_____

_____ **6.** A major victory for the <u>Axis Powers</u> occurred in the D-Day invasion on the beaches of Normandy, France.

_____

**DIRECTIONS** Look up three of the vocabulary terms in the word bank. On a separate piece of paper, write the dictionary definition of the word that is closest to the definition used in your textbook.

# Modern European History

## Vocabulary Builder

### Section 3

| | | |
|---|---|---|
| arms race | Berlin Wall | Cold War |
| common market | ethnic tensions | European Union (EU) |
| reunification | superpowers | |

**DIRECTIONS** Read each sentence and fill in the blank with the word from the word pair that best completes the sentence.

1. The United States and the Soviet Union were rivals in the

   _____. (**Cold War/European Union**)

2. The _____ of East and West Germany came in 1989 when the Berlin Wall was torn down. (**common market/reunification**)

3. After the Cold War, _____ led to the breakup of Czechoslovakia and Yugoslavia. (**superpowers/ethnic tensions**)

4. Belgium, France, Italy, Luxembourg, the Netherlands, and West Germany were the first countries to form a common market, which is now known as the

   _____. (**superpowers/European Union**)

5. The high costs of the _____ hurt the Soviet Union. (**arms race/Berlin Wall**)

**DIRECTIONS** Choose five of the vocabulary words from the word bank. On a separate sheet of paper, write a summary of what you learned in the section using these terms.

# Anne Frank

## 1929–1945

**HOW SHE AFFECTED THE WORLD**
Anne Frank is one of the most well-known Holocaust victims. In her diary, published after her death, Anne describes life during the two years she spent hiding from the Nazis. She always remained optimistic, writing, "In spite of everything I still believe that people are really good at heart."

*As you read the biography below,* think about the perseverance Anne must have had to survive in hiding for so long.

## VOCABULARY

**emigrated** left one's country

**Secret Annexe** nickname Anne gave the attic

**confidante** someone with whom to trust personal matters

**Gestapo** Nazi police

**typhus** disease spread by ticks and fleas

Originally from Germany, Anne Frank's family **emigrated** to Amsterdam, Holland, when the Nazis came into power in 1933. In 1941, the Germans invaded Holland. When Anne's older sister Margot received an order in July 1942 to report for deportation to a labor camp, the family went into hiding in a back-room office. Soon after, another Jewish couple and their son and an elderly dentist joined them in the "**Secret Annexe.**"

Anne took into hiding a diary she had received a month earlier for her birthday. She addressed it as "Kitty" and considered it her closest friend and **confidante**.

Anne not only wrote about her ordeal hiding from the Nazis and the tensions that grew between the eight people hiding together, but also about her daily life as a teenager. Labeled a "chatterbox," it was hard for Anne to remain quiet all day. In her October 1, 1942, diary entry, she wrote, "We are as quiet as mice. Who, three months ago, would ever have guessed that quicksilver Anne would have to sit still for hours—and, what's more, could?" Anne spent most of her time writing and studying.

The **Gestapo** discovered the Franks on August 4, 1944, and the family was sent to the Auschwitz death camp, where Mrs. Frank died. Anne and her sister, who were transferred to the Bergen-Belsen death camp, both died there of **typhus** in 1945.

After raiding the Frank's hideout, German soldiers had scattered the diary pages on the floor. When Mr. Frank, the only family member to survive the Holocaust, returned to Amsterdam, he was given his daughter's diary, which became a best-selling book. Anne's story has also been turned into a play, a movie, and an opera. The original diary is on display at the Franks' hiding place in Amsterdam, now a museum.

## WHAT DID YOU LEARN?

**1. Recall** Summarize the major events in Anne Frank's life.

_____

_____

**2. Evaluate** Why do you think such a young girl became one of the most important figures from the Holocaust?

_____

_____

## ACTIVITY

Using the information you learned about Anne in the reading, write an epitaph—a writing that is done in memory of someone who has died—that captures her personality and spirit.

**Modern European History**                    Biography

# Vladimir Lenin
## 1870–1924

**HOW HE AFFECTED THE WORLD**
Vladimir Lenin was a Russian **revolutionary** who changed the course of European history by establishing a Communist Soviet Union.

*As you read the biography below,* *think about how Lenin's determination affected Russia's history for much of the 1900s.*

© The Granger Collection, New York

Vladimir Lenin became a revolutionary as a young adult, around same the time his brother was executed for conspiring to assassinate the Russian **czar**. He was banished from studying at a university for his activities, but he finished his law studies independently. He practiced law briefly before focusing on Marxism—the belief that a society will naturally progress from capitalism to communism.

Lenin spent much of the years between 1895 and 1917 either banished from Russia or in voluntary **exile**. During this time, he developed and wrote about a branch of Marxism that called for a **proletariat** revolution to bring about communism. Namely, he wanted the working class to overthrow the **bourgeoisie** and establish a classless society. This means that land and property are owned in common, not by individuals. Lenin believed in achieving this by force.

World War I proved the perfect opportunity for Lenin to stage his revolution. He believed this war

**VOCABULARY**
**revolutionary** one who fights for radical change
**czar** emperor
**exile** forced absence from your country
**proletariat** working class
**bourgeoisie** class that owns most of the wealth

was caused by greed on both sides for land. After
three years at war, Russian peasants supported
Lenin's plan for peace with Germany. The German
government supported Lenin's plan as well.

In 1917 Lenin and his Bolshevik Party (his
brand of Marxism) took power. They established
a Soviet government with Lenin as their leader.
The government kept its promise of peace with
Germany by signing a treaty. They also ended
private ownership of land and distributed it among
the working class. Factory workers finally had
control over their production—in theory. Lenin
set up a Communist dictatorship and put down all
opposition.

After his death in 1924, his body was specially
preserved and placed on display in Moscow. It is
still on display.

## WHAT DID YOU LEARN?

**1. Identify** What were some of the major components of Lenin's political beliefs?

_____

_____

**2. Evaluate** Do you think Lenin was a popular leader in his country? Give reasons
for your answer.

_____

_____

## ACTIVITY

Suppose that it is October 1917, and you are Vladimir Lenin. You are
about to give your first speech as the new, victorious leader of Russia.
What will you say to the men and women of your country? Write your
speech on a separate piece of paper.

# Animal Farm
## by George Orwell

**ABOUT THE READING** This excerpt is from the novel *Animal Farm* by George Orwell. In this fable, farm animals revolt against humans and take control of their farm, setting up their own government. Originally published in 1945, the book is an **allegory** that represents Russia under Stalin's dictatorship.

**VOCABULARY**

**allegory** work in which the characters and events symbolize a deeper meaning

**rations** limited amount of something, such as food

**Animalism** fictional form of government

*As you read the passage below,* decide whether Squealer is a character you can trust.

Meanwhile life was hard. The winter was as cold as the last one had been, and food was even shorter. Once again all **rations** were reduced, except those of the pigs and the dogs. A too rigid equality in rations, Squealer explained, would have been contrary to the principles of **Animalism**. In any case he had no difficulty in proving to the other animals that they were *not* in reality short of food, whatever the appearances might be. For the time being, certainly, it had been found necessary to make a readjustment of rations (Squealer always spoke of it as a "readjustment," never as a "reduction"), but in comparison with the days of Jones, the improvement was enormous. Reading out the figures in a shrill, rapid voice, he proved to them in detail that they had more oats, more hay, more turnips than they had had in Jones's day, that they worked shorter hours, that their drinking water was of better quality, that they lived longer, that a larger proportion of their young ones survived infancy,

> **Why do you think rations are not reduced for pigs and dogs?**
> _____
> _____

> **Why doesn't Squealer want to use the word "reduction"?**
> _____
> _____

From *Animal Farm* by George Orwell. Copyright 1946 by **Harcourt, Inc.;** copyright renewed © 1974 by Sonia Orwell. Reproduced by permission of the publisher.

**Animal Farm,** *continued*                                          Literature

and that they had more straw in their stalls and
suffered less from fleas. The animals believed every
word of it. Truth to tell, Jones and all he stood for
had almost faded out of their memories. They
knew that life nowadays was harsh and bare, that
they were often hungry and often cold, and that
they were usually working when they were not
asleep. But doubtless it had been worse in the old
days. They were glad to believe so. Besides, in those
days they had been slaves and now they were free,
and that made all the difference, as Squealer did not
fail to point out.

> Underline details in the passage
> that help you decide what life is
> really like for the animals.

## ANALYZING LITERATURE

1. **Main Idea** According to the passage, how successful do you think Animalism has
   been for this society?

   _____

   _____

2. **Critical Thinking: Drawing Inferences** What kind of animal do you think
   Squealer is, and what is his role in this society? Give reasons for your answer.

   _____

   _____

## ACTIVITY

Create an outline for an allegory you might write to symbolize the Cold
War. Choose one animal to represent the United States and another to
represent the Soviet Union.

# Charter of the United Nations

**ABOUT THE READING** The United Nations (UN) was established in 1945, following two very destructive world wars. The goal was to find a way that all countries of the world could exist together peacefully. The following reading outlines the purpose of the UN.

*As you read,* imagine that it is 1945 and you are the leader of a small European country. How would you feel about the establishment of the United Nations?

**VOCABULARY**
**preamble** introduction
**succeeding** following next in order
**scourge** devastation
**fundamental** basic
**machinery** means of achieving a result

## PREAMBLE

WE THE PEOPLES OF THE UNITED NATIONS DETERMINED

- to save **succeeding** generations from the **scourge** of war, which twice in our lifetime has brought untold sorrow to mankind, and

- to reaffirm faith in **fundamental** human rights, in the dignity and worth of the human person, in the equal rights of men and women and of nations large and small, and

- to establish conditions under which justice and respect for the obligations arising from treaties and other sources of international law can be maintained, and

> The UN helps make sure that countries follow the agreements made in treaties.

- to promote social progress and better standards of life in larger freedom,

"United Nations Preamble" from *United Nations* web site accessed at www.un.com/aboutuncharter/preamble.htm. Copyright 2000–2005 by United Nations. Reproduced by permission of **The Secretary of the Publications Board, United Nations, New York, NY.**

AND FOR THESE ENDS

- to practice tolerance and live together in peace with one another as good neighbours, and

> Countries must respect one another and accept differences, such as religious or cultural.

- to unite our strength to maintain international peace and security, and

- to ensure, by the acceptance of principles and the institution of methods, that armed force shall not be used, save in the common interest, and

> Military action is to be avoided unless it is deemed necessary by the UN.

- to employ international **machinery** for the promotion of the economic and social advancement of all peoples,

HAVE RESOLVED TO COMBINE OUR EFFORTS TO ACCOMPLISH THESE AIMS[.]

Accordingly, our respective Governments, through representatives assembled in the city of San Francisco, who have exhibited their full powers found to be in good and due form, have agreed to the present Charter of the United Nations and do hereby establish an international organization to be known as the United Nations.

## WHAT DID YOU LEARN?

1. **Identify** In your own words, name three goals of the UN, as set forth in the Charter.

_____

_____

2. **Draw Conclusions** If the UN had existed in 1914, how might it have prevented World War I?

_____

_____

3. **Predict** What current global issue do you think could be solved by the UN? Give reasons for your answer.

_____

_____

**Modern European History**          Geography and History

# Europe and World War I

World War I transformed Europe in many ways and changed the
borders of many countries. Some countries separated or combined,
and many gained their independence.

## MAP ACTIVITY

**1.** Use a green pencil or marker to shade the countries of the Allied Powers.

**2.** Use an orange pencil or marker to shade the countries of the Central Powers.

**3.** Use a blue pencil or marker to shade the countries that were neutral.

Europe and World War I, *continued*                    Geography and History

## ANALYZING MAPS

1. **Location**  Where was the capital of Russia in 1914 located? (Be as specific as you can.)

_____

_____

2. **Movement**  Why do you think Germany invaded France and Belgium first?

_____

_____

3. **Location**  Which side do you think had an advantage in the war? Why?

_____

_____

4. **Comparing and Contrasting**  Based on location, what challenges did the United States face when they entered the war? What advantages did they have?

_____

_____

5. **Comparing and Contrasting**  How was the map of Europe the same after World War I? How was it different?

_____

_____

**Modern European History**

# Social Studies Skills

## Critical Thinking

# Interpreting Political Cartoons

### LEARN THE SKILL

Political cartoons are drawings that express views on important political or social issues. The ability to interpret them will help you understand current or historical issues and people's attitudes about them.

### PRACTICE THE SKILL

Examine the cartoon of Hitler and Stalin on this page. Before World War II, they had agreed not to attack each other. Answer the following questions to interpret the message of the cartoon.

WONDER HOW LONG THE HONEYMOON WILL LAST?

© The Granger Collection, New York

**1.** When was this cartoon probably published?

_____

**2.** What emotions are Hitler and Stalin showing in this cartoon?

_____

**3.** What is the message of this cartoon?

_____

**Modern European History**                    Geography for Life

# The Soviet "Game of the Name"

Where were you born? St. Petersburg. Where did you grow up?
Petrograd. Where do you live? Leningrad. Where would you like to live?
St. Petersburg. This joke was published in *The Economist* magazine in
1991. Why is it a joke? Because St. Petersburg-Petrograd-Leningrad-
St. Petersburg are all names of a single place, the city founded on the
shores of the Baltic Sea in 1703 by Peter I of Russia. St. Petersburg is
not the only place in Russia to experience official renaming. Scores of
towns and cities (and other features) in Russia and the rest of the Soviet
Union had politically motivated name changes during the 75 years of
Soviet rule.

   In general, *toponyms* (place-names) are mirrors of the societies that
choose them. The Soviet use of toponyms demonstrates the wish to
influence people's opinions. In various times and places, toponyms
reveal their namers' religious beliefs, practical bent, sense of humor,
cultural or national icons and heroes, and many other attitudes and
traits. Toponyms help turn places into symbols of folk or popular culture.

   Soon after obtaining power, the Soviets wiped off the map names that
belonged to Russia's czarist past. These old names were replaced with
the names of revolutionaries and leaders of the Communist Party and
Soviet Union. If those same revolutionaries and leaders later became
unpopular, their names were removed and new ones were chosen. For
example, in the 1920s and 1930s there were half a dozen cities named
for Joseph Stalin. However, in 1961, then-president Nikita Khrushchev
changed them all after Stalin's crimes were revealed. Some cities
experienced as many as four name changes as a result of the shifting
winds of political fortune. In addition to Soviet communist leaders,
other categories of people honored with toponyms included
revolutionaries and communists from other times and places and those
who had made major (and, of course, politically correct) contributions
to Russian or Soviet arts and sciences.

## YOU ARE THE GEOGRAPHER

The table on the page following the map contains 10 cities in Russia and
Ukraine. This is just a sample of the many cities that experienced the
Soviet "game of the name." Begin by using your textbook or an atlas to
correctly label these on the map using their current names. (If you have
an old atlas, you may have to look under a previous name.)

**The Soviet "Game of the Name",** *continued*          Geography for Life

Next, use classroom resources to look up the underlined names (your teacher may choose to assign one or several of the names to you, rather than have you look up every name yourself). When you are reading about these people, note any deeds that would have made them villains or heroes (or both, at different times!) to the Soviet Union's communist leaders. Pay attention to the pattern of dates of city name changes. They often come in clusters, reflecting some major Soviet ideological shift.

Write about what you learned. Share it in a group discussion. Can you come up with place-names in your state or region that honor exceptional people? Do you know of any that have been changed out of a desire to forget someone's less than honorable deeds?

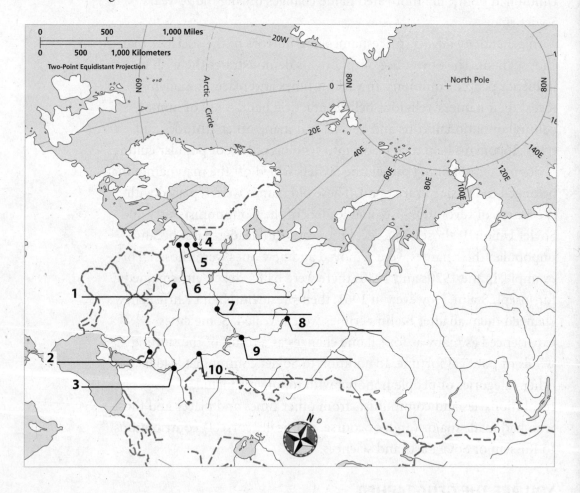

## Selected Russian and Ukrainian City Names

| Current city name, date acquired, & person named for | Recent city population figures | Former city name, dates applicable, & person named for | Former city name, dates applicable, & person named for | Former city name, dates applicable, & person named for |
|---|---|---|---|---|
| *St. Petersburg* 1991 St. Peter | 4,952,000 | Leningrad 1924–1991 V. I. Lenin | Petrograd 1914–1924 St. Peter; also Peter I (the Great) | St. Petersburg 1703–1914 St. Peter |
| *Gatchina* 1944 | 81,300 | Trotsk 1923–1929 L. D. Trotsky | Krasnogvardeysk 1929–1944 | Gatchina 1795–1923 |
| *Volgograd* 1961 [Volga River] | 1,006,000 | Stalingrad 1925–1961 I. V. Stalin | Tsaritsyn Before 1925 | |
| *Luhansk, Ukraine* 1990 | 504,000 | Voroshilovgrad 1970–1989 & 1935–1958 K. Y. Voroshilov | Lugansk 1797–1935 & 1958–1970 | Yekaterinoslav 1795–1797 Catherine II (the Great) |
| *Perm* 1957 | 1,099,000 | Molotov 1940–1957 V. M. Molotov | Perm 1780–1940 | |
| *Naberezhnyye Chelny* 1988 | 514,000 | Brezhnev 1982–1988 L. I. Brezhnev | Naberezhnyye Chelny 1930–1982 | Chelny Before 1930 |
| *Engels* 1931 F. Engels | 183,000 | Pokrovsk Before 1931 | | |
| *Gagarin* 1968 Y. A. Gagarin | Not known | Gzhatsk Before 1968 | | |
| *Nizhniy Novgorod* 1990 | 3,704,000 | Gorky 1932–1990 M. Gorky | Nizhniy Novgorod Before 1932 | |
| *Pushkin* 1937 A. S. Pushkin | 95,300 | Petsokye Selo 1918–1937 (means Children's Village) | Tsarskoye Selo 1728–1918 (means Tsar's Village) | |

**Modern European History**                    Critical Thinking

## Disaster at Chernobyl

*The world's worst nuclear accident took place at the Chernobyl Nuclear Power Plant in Ukraine, in what was then the Soviet Union. To learn about this event, which threatened the health and well-being of millions of people, study the information and answer the questions that follow.*

Early Saturday morning, April 26, 1986, the unthinkable occurred. An explosion at Cherynobyl's reactor number 4 blew the unit apart. The accident occurred in just two minutes. The tragedy took longer to unfold.

As the reactor was shutting down for routine maintenance, engineers decided to test the operation of its emergency cooling systems under reduced power. With the cooling pumps slowed, the temperature and size of the nuclear reaction inside the core began to increase. This set in motion a series of events that quickly led to catastrophe.

---

### Time Line to Disaster

**1:03 a.m.** Operators turn off emergency shutdown devices so they can manually change some settings during the test. They also restart some water pumps to ensure proper cooling after the test.

**1:23 a.m.** Realizing they are about to lose control, operators try to shut down. It is too late. The nuclear reaction reaches 100 times the reactor's capacity.

**1:22 a.m.** A computer warning says to shut down. The added coolant has dropped steam production in the reactor. This lack of steam has raised the nuclear reaction to dangerous levels. Instead, operators try to complete the test.

**1:24 a.m.** The core disintegrates and hot fuel comes into contact with the coolant. A tremendous steam build-up blows the roof off the reactor, spewing radioactive materials into the atmosphere.

---

Not until Monday evening, April 28, when Scandinavian monitoring devices detected major increases in radiation levels in their countries, did the Soviet government reveal the accident to the world. Meanwhile, high-level winds were spreading the radioactive fallout across Europe.

Except for those who lived near Chernobyl, most Ukrainians did not suffer immediate effects from the blast. They were inside their homes, in bed, when it occurred. Farmers in Poland who went to work in the fields on Monday morning were not as lucky. Their skin started itching and then they began to vomit. Their hands swelled and their hair fell out as their radiation sickness worsened.

**Disaster at Chernobyl,** *continued*                                    Critical Thinking

Radioactive rain in Scandinavia led to high levels of radiation in the soil. In East Germany, where radiation levels were 100 times higher than normal, people were warned not to eat fresh fruit or fish, or drink milk. The British government issued warnings about drinking rainwater and banned the slaughter of sheep for food in parts of Wales and Scotland, where the grass was contaminated with radiation.

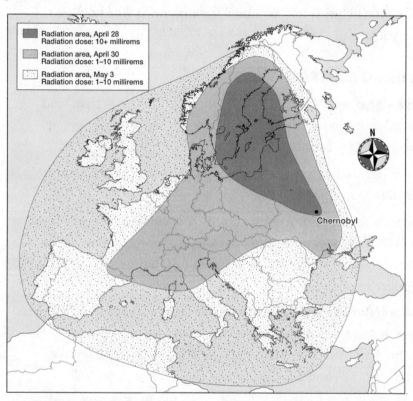

Despite such precautions, scientists estimate that over the next several decades nearly 300,000 Europeans may die from cancers that are related to radiation exposure from Chernobyl. The number of abnormal births and other genetic defects is much harder to predict.

**1.** Why did the Polish farmers get sick while East German and Swedish farmers did not?

_____

**2.** In what direction was the wind blowing on April 27? On April 29? How do you know?

_____

**3.** Were the people of southern England or northern Italy exposed to more radiation? How do you know?

_____

# Using Context Clues–Contrast

When you read, you may come across words or phrases with which you are not familiar. Instead of skipping over them, use context clues—words and sentences before and after the word or phrase you do not understand—to make an educated guess at its meaning. A contrast clue is a type of context clue. It tells you how the unknown word differs from words you already know.

## TIPS FOR USING CONTRAST CLUES

- **Look for signal words.** Signal words such as *but, rather than,* and *however* tell you that a phrase that means the opposite of the one before or after it is coming.

  Example: The soldier wanted to *abandon* her post, *but she knew it was her duty to stay put*.

  The signal word *but* tells you that a phrase is coming up—*to stay put*—which likely will mean the opposite of the word *abandon*. In this case, the signal word helps you figure out that *to stay put* means the opposite of *abandon*, or *to leave*.

- **What word(s) mean the opposite of the one you know?** When you read a sentence, think about what the antonyms are of the word(s) you know. Antonyms are words that are opposites—for example, *open* and *shut, rich* and *poor, fast* and *slow,* and *short* and *tall*.

  Example: *Can peace be best reached through negotiation, not conflict?*

  Think about words that mean the opposite of *conflict*—for example, *getting along, cooperating, finding solutions,* and *not fighting*. Using these antonyms for *conflict*, you can figure out that *negotiation* likely means something similar to these antonyms—*coming to an agreement*.

- **Replace the unknown word to test its meaning.** As a check of whether you have determined the correct meaning of an unknown word, replace it in the sentence with a synonym—a word that is similar in meaning. Examples of synonyms are *rich* and *wealthy, small* and *tiny,* and *loud* and *noisy*.

  Example: *The economy faltered while trade between the two countries grew.*

Using contrast clues, let's say that you think that *faltered* means *declined*. To check that you are correct, try using synonyms for *faltered* and *declined*. For example, you might try using *slowed* and *stumbled*. Ask yourself: Do these words change the original meaning of the sentence? Since they do not, you have correctly figured out the meaning of *faltered—declined*. Congratulations!

## PRACTICING USING CONTRAST CLUES

**Directions**  Use contrast clues to determine the meaning of the underlined word in the following sentences. Describe how you arrived at your answer.

**1.** Trenches dug in <u>zigzag</u> patterns prevented the enemy from firing down the length of a trench.

_____

_____

**2.** Instead of accepting the differences between people in the population, Hitler began <u>discriminating</u> against people such as Jews.

_____

_____

**3.** Rather than oppose separate governments, The Czechs and the Slovaks <u>advocated</u> for separation.

_____

_____

## EVALUATING

**4. Evaluating Your Definitions**  Now look up the underlined words in the dictionary. How close were your own definitions?

**Rubric**

• Did you accurately determine the meaning of each word?

• Now that you know what the words mean, were there other clues from the excerpts that you didn't notice at first?

• On a separate sheet of paper, list at least three ways that being able to use contrast clues for word meaning can be helpful.

**Modern European History**

# Focus on Writing

## Writing a Diary Entry

Some people keep diaries to record important events in their lives, to learn about themselves, or even to become a better writer. Writing a diary entry from someone else's point of view can help you to understand that person's life and experiences, too.

### PREWRITING

1. **Writing about World War I** Write one or two events from World War I that you could include in a diary entry. From what viewpoint might you describe the events?

   For example: the outbreak of the war, told from the point of view of a child living in France

   _____

   _____

   _____

2. **Telling about World War II** What information about World War II might you include in a diary entry? Will you write from the point of view of a supporter of the Allies or the Axis? Jot down some ideas.

   For example: the hiding of a Jewish family, told from the point of view of the person hiding them

   _____

   _____

   _____

3. **Thinking about Europe since 1945** Add details about Europe during this time. Think of one event you might write about in your diary entry.

   For example: the fall of the Berlin Wall, told from the point of view of a man from East Germany whose brother lives in West Germany

   _____

   _____

   _____

# WRITING

4. **Writing a Diary Entry** Choose an imaginary character who might have taken part in an event discussed in the chapter. You might choose, for example, a soldier who fought in the trenches, or a member of the Jewish uprising in Warsaw, Poland. Write a diary entry from the point of view of the character you selected.

Remember to describe the event and your character's feelings about the event. Give vivid descriptions. Try to picture what the person smells, tastes, and hears as well as sees. You might describe the weather, or how it physically feels to be wherever the person is.

# EVALUATING AND PROOFREADING

5. **Evaluating Your Diary Entry** Ask a friend or classmate to read your diary entry, then tell you what they learned about the person through your entry. Use the questions below to evaluate and revise your diary entry.

**Rubric**

- Does your diary entry give a good sense of who the person is and what he or she is doing?

- Does your diary entry give details that make it clear what historical period you are writing about?

- Does your diary entry give a clear depiction of the event(s) about which you chose to write?

- Is your diary entry vivid? Do you give details pertaining to all five senses?

6. **Proofreading Your Diary Entry** Last, check the following:

- Capitalization and spelling of all proper names and places

- Punctuation, grammar, and spelling

## Modern European History

# Chapter Review

**BIG IDEAS**

1. World War 1 and the peace treaty that followed brought tremendous change to Europe.
2. Problems in Europe led to World War II, the deadliest war in history.
3. After years of division during the Cold War, today Europe is working toward unity.

## REVIEWING VOCABULARY, TERMS, AND PLACES

Use the description in the right column to unscramble the term in the box. Write the correct term in the space provided.

| LTAOINNSMAI |
| --- |

1. _____ devotion and loyalty to one's country

| NCTHER FRWERAA |
| --- |

2. _____ style of fighting in World War I

| OTSCOHUAL |
| --- |

3. _____ attempt by the Nazis to destroy the Jews

| TCDOITRA |
| --- |

4. _____ a ruler who has total control of a country

| LCDO RWA |
| --- |

5. _____ period of time in which the superpowers competed in a nuclear arms race

## COMPREHENSION AND CRITICAL THINKING

Read the **FALSE** statement below. On the line provided, replace the underlined word to make this statement true.

1. During World War I, there was a/an <u>conflict</u> between Britain, France, and Russia.

_____

2. Tensions between Austria-Hungary and <u>Russia</u> sparked World War I.

_____

3. The stock market crash of 1929 triggered a global economic crisis known as the <u>Holocaust</u>.

_____

**4.** Adolf Hitler was the leader of Germany's <u>Communist</u> government.

_____

**5.** Following the Cold War, many Eastern European countries changed forms
of <u>alliances</u>.

_____

## REVIEWING THEMES

In the space provided, explain how each term relates to the theme
listed below.

    **Theme:** *regions*

**1.** nationalism

_____

**2.** Treaty of Versailles

_____

    **Theme:** *movement*

**3.** Berlin Wall

_____

**4.** European Union

_____

## REVIEW ACTIVITY: TIME LINE

Tape at least three sheets of paper together and create a time line that
shows the history of Europe from 1900 to the present. Cut out or
draw maps of Europe and paste them on the time line to show how
boundaries and countries changed throughout this period. Be sure
to cover World War I, World War II, and the Cold War.

# Reading and Writing Allegories

## OVERVIEW/PURPOSE

Have students read *Animal Farm* by George Orwell and discuss the book—and the form of allegory—in detail. Then, ask each student to choose a historical figure from twentieth century Europe and enroll that person in your school. Write an allegory about the historical figure's experience as a student in a twenty-first century American middle school. Encourage students to use humor in their allegories.

## PLANNING

### Time Suggested

Four 45-minute blocks and one and a half weeks of outside class time (homework time)

### Materials

*Animal Farm* by George Orwell

### Resources

Handout: Writing Your Allegory
Rubric: Standards for Evaluating Your Work

### Preparation

- Allow time to discuss *Animal Farm* and the form of allegory in class.
- Schedule library time for each student to research his or her historical figure.

### Group Size

Students will work individually.

## OBJECTIVES

- Understand the literary form of allegory.
- Read and analyze *Animal Farm* as an allegorical novel.
- Research and understand a person from modern European history in depth.
- Understand the use of symbolism.

## PROCEDURE

1. Distribute copies of *Animal Farm* and have students read the book at home over the course of two or three weeks.

2. Use a class period to analyze the book, focusing heavily on symbolism as a literary technique, as well as the symbolism used in the book.

3. Distribute copies of **Handout 1: "Writing Your Allegory"** and **Handout 2: "Standards for Evaluating Your Work."** Have students read the information aloud. As a class, brainstorm allegories that might be written about a topic familiar to them. Make sure students become comfortable with this genre before asking them to write their own allegory.

4. As a class, come up with a list of historical figures from twentieth century Europe that students might choose. Try to create an extensive list to give students many options. The people do not have to be solely from the chapter on Modern European History; they can represent artists, musicians, writers, or any well-known European from the twentieth century.

5. As homework, have students spend three nights working on their allegories. The first night, ask them to choose their theme and write an outline for their allegory. The second night, ask them to write the first draft. On the third night, students can edit and revise their allegories.

## EXTEND

1. Read some of the allegories out loud. See if other students can recognize the historical figure in the story. What other metaphors can they recognize about their school?

2. Discuss other forms of allegory—for example, its use in sculpture, art, film, or photography. Ask students to find an example of one of these other forms and bring it in to share with the rest of the class.

# Writing Your Allegory

1. **Understand the word** *allegory*. Remember, it is a representation of an idea or concept in symbolic form. For this assignment, you will be writing a story that will serve as an allegory, using *Animal Farm* as a model.

2. **Choose one or two key elements of your school on which to focus.** For example, if sports are a major focus of your school, let that be a focus of your story. Or you might focus on the location of your school, whether it is an urban setting or rural setting. Jot down several key characteristics of your school to help you get started.

3. **Research the historical figure you have chosen thoroughly.** Make sure you learn as much as you can about the person's background, personality, political beliefs, and so on.

4. **Choose a setting within your school for your allegory.** For example, consider the school cafeteria or library. Think about what you are trying to represent symbolically, and the best setting to do that.

5. **Create a simple plot, or series of events, for your allegory.** In *Animal Farm*, the animals decided to take control of their farm and establish their own government. Perhaps your historical figure has decided to take control of the cafeteria and establish his or her own set of rules for it. Keep it simple and focused, and remember to have fun with it.

**Modern European History**            Interdisciplinary Project

# Standards for Evaluating Your Work

## RUBRIC

- Did you create a simple, clear plot?

- Did you use an appropriate setting for your plot?

- Did you represent your school in a symbolic way?

- Do other students recognize and relate to the symbolic representations in your story?

- Can other students recognize the historical character in your story?

- Even though your historical character is in a fictional setting, did you portray his or her personality and beliefs accurately?

- Did you provide a situation that allowed your historical character to demonstrate his or her personality and beliefs?

- Did you edit and revise your allegory?

- Did you proofread your allegory and make any necessary corrections in spelling, punctuation, and grammar?

# Modern European History

## Teacher's Interdisciplinary Project

### Civics, Government, and Social Studies

## Current Events: Letting Historical Figures Solve Today's Problems

### OVERVIEW/PURPOSE

Each student will choose an important person from twentieth century Europe to portray. They may choose a specific person, such as Vladimir Lenin, or make a more generic choice, such as a French soldier. Then the students will choose a global issue for their characters to solve. The students will create a discussion, allowing each member of the group to try to persuade the others that his or her solution is the best.

### PLANNING

#### Time Suggested

Three 45-minute blocks

#### Materials

Several issues of recent newspapers

#### Preparation

- Schedule library time for each student to research his or her "character."

- Bring in several recent newspapers to allow students to choose the issue for discussion. (Students may need to do additional research on the topic they choose.)

#### Group Size

Students will work in groups of 3–4.

### OBJECTIVES

- Conduct research about an important historical figure from Europe in the 1900s to gain an understanding of his or her political beliefs.

- Gain an understanding of a current issue.

- Create a compelling argument to help resolve the issue.

- See how points of view can differ and be supported by different reasons and evidence.

## PROCEDURE

1. Each group should choose a current issue that is important to people all over the world.

2. Tell students to read several newspaper or magazine articles on the issue their group chooses. Direct them to use library and Internet resources to locate relevant articles. Students should take notes on the different views people have about the issue. They should try to understand the issue from at least two different points of view.

3. Have students chose a European person from the 1900s. They should research this person, to try to determine what his or her views on the issue likely would be. For example, Lenin would likely be opposed to the spread of democracy and market economies throughout the world. Students should prepare a written summary of what the person's views on the issue would likely be.

4. Each group should then discuss the issue from the viewpoint of the European person they chose, speaking in turn. This discussion can take place in front of the whole class (with you serving as the moderator) or in separate areas around the classroom. If the latter, one person from each group should serve as note-taker and another as moderator. Then have the group report back on the results of their discussions.

## EXTEND

Have a class discussion in which students discuss political leaders of today and how they might have reacted to the events of World War I, World War II, and the Cold War. For example, how do students think the current President of the United States would have dealt with Hitler? Ask students for reasons for their answers.

# Vocabulary Builder

| | | |
|---|---|---|
| Mediterranean Sea | Pyrenees | Apennines |
| Alps | Mediterranean climate | plains |
| undersea mountains | | |

**DIRECTIONS** On the line provided before each statement, write **T** if a statement is true and **F** if a statement is false. If the statement is false, write the term from the word bank that would make the statement true on the line after each sentence.

_____ **1.** The <u>Alps</u> form a boundary between Spain and France.

_____

_____ **2.** Islands and <u>peninsulas</u> form the region of Southern Europe.

_____

_____ **3.** The <u>Apennines</u> are Europe's highest mountain range.

_____

_____ **4.** The countries of Southern Europe all share a common location on the <u>Adriatic Sea</u>.

_____

_____ **5.** The <u>Pyrenees</u> run along the Italian Peninsula.

_____

**DIRECTIONS** Read each sentence and fill in the blank with the word in the word pair that best completes the sentence.

**6.** Many of Southern Europe's islands are formed by _____.
**(undersea mountains/plains)**

**7.** The _____ is ideal for growing a variety of crops.
**(Mediterranean Sea/Mediterranean climate)**

**Southern Europe**

| | | |
|---|---|---|
| Athens | Alexander the Great | Byzantine Empire |
| Roman Empire | Orthodox Church | monarchy |
| philosophy | democracy | |

**DIRECTIONS** Write three words or phrases that describe the term.

**1.** democracy_____

**2.** monarchy _____

**3.** philosophy_____

**DIRECTIONS** Look at each set of vocabulary terms. On the line provided, write the letter of the term that does not relate to the others.

_____ **4. a.** theater        _____ **5. a.** Orthodox Church
        **b.** philosophy                  **b.** Parthenon
        **c.** democracy                   **c.** Byzantine Empire
        **d.** population                   **d.** Christianity

**DIRECTIONS** Choose five of the words from the word bank. Use the words to write a summary of what you learned in the section.

_____

_____

_____

_____

_____

_____

_____

_____

_____

**Southern Europe**                    Vocabulary Builder

| | | | |
|---|---|---|---|
| Rome | Renaissance | nationalism | dictatorship |
| pope | Vatican City | Sicily | Naples |
| Milan | | | |

**DIRECTIONS** Read each sentence and fill in the blank with the word in the word pair that best completes the sentence.

1. _____, or strong patriotic feelings for a country, led people across Italy to fight for unification. (**Nationalism/ Renaissance**)

2. The _____ is the head of the Roman Catholic church. (**pope/prime minister**)

3. _____ is an independent state located within the city of Rome. (**Venice/Vatican City**)

4. _____, Italy's capital, has ties to both northern and southern Italy. (**Rome/Naples**)

5. The island of _____ at Italy's southern tip depends on agriculture for its survival. (**Milan/Sicily**)

6. _____ is a center for industry and fashion design. (**Naples/Milan**)

**DIRECTIONS** Choose five of the words from the word bank. On a separate piece of paper use these words to write a poem, story, or letter that relates to the section.

**Southern Europe**                          Vocabulary Builder

Section 4

| | | |
|---|---|---|
| Lisbon | republic | Madrid |
| fado | flamenco | parliamentary monarchy |
| Barcelona | Iberia | |

**DIRECTIONS**  Answer each question by writing a sentence that contains
at least one word from the word bank.

1. Describe one cultural contribution of Spain or Portugal in the area of music
   or art.

   _____

   _____

2. How are Spain and Portugal governed today?

   _____

   _____

3. Where are the centers of industry, tourism, and culture in Spain?

   _____

   _____

4. Where are the industries of Portugal based?

   _____

   _____

**DIRECTIONS**  Look at each set of terms. On the line provided, write the
letter of the term that does not relate to the others.

_____  **5. a.** Basque      **b.** Catalan      **c.** Galician      **d.** Lisbon

_____  **6. a.** Muslim      **b.** Greek        **c.** Roman         **d.** Portuguese

**Southern Europe**

Biography

# Aristotle
384 BC–322 BC

**HOW HE AFFECTED THE WORLD** Aristotle was one of the most influential philosophers in history. His ideas about science and logic transformed Western thought.

Bettmann/CORBIS

*As you read the biography below,* think about how Aristotle's ideas affect the modern world.

Aristotle lived during a time when there was no state-of-the-art scientific equipment to view cells or send man into outer space. Yet, Aristotle used his observations of the world to write **treatises** that continue to contribute to the arts and sciences today. Aristotle was born in northern Greece as a son of a doctor for the royal family of **Macedonia**. He is believed to have been schooled in medicine and was sent to Athens to study philosophy under **Plato** at about the age of seventeen. Aristotle was considered a brilliant student and when Plato died, he began traveling and studying on his own.

In 338 BC Aristotle was invited to Macedonia to tutor King Philip II's heir and son, who later became known as Alexander the Great. When Alexander ascended the throne, Aristotle returned to Athens and set up his own school known as the Lyceum.

Upon the death of Alexander the Great, anti-Macedonian feelings broke out in Athens. Aristotle feared for his life and was forced to flee due to his strong Macedonian connections. He died soon after on the Greek island of Euboea.

Aristotle originated the formal study of logic. During his lifetime, he wrote on nearly all areas of science, from **astronomy** to **zoology**. He determined

## VOCABULARY

**treatise** a written argument using a particular method

**Macedonia** an ancient kingdom of northern Greece that became part of a larger empire under Philip II and Alexander the Great

**Plato** an ancient Greek philosopher

**astronomy** the science of objects and matter in outer space

**zoology** the study of animals

**surpassed** exceeded or improved upon

Europe and Russia

Aristotle, *continued*                                          Biography

that all objects, including organisms, are made up
of matter—or their composed material—but that
in reality, they are given a form, or their potential
shape.

Aristotle developed the study of the weather as
well as the classification of animals. He is the reason
animals have two-part scientific names: the genus,
or category of animals, and the species, which
describe their characteristics.

Aristotle's writings have been translated into
dozens of languages and have been studied and
admired by philosophers and thinkers throughout
history. His writings about nature were adopted by
Jews, Christians, and Muslims as consistent with
their ideas about faith. His ideas about government
influenced Thomas Jefferson, the author of the U.S.
Declaration of Independence. Although many of
Aristotle's theories of science have been **surpassed**,
his treatises and philosophies continue to be a
leading field of study and debate today.

## WHAT DID YOU LEARN?

**1. Recall** Why did Aristotle leave Athens upon the death of Alexander the Great?

_____

_____

**2. Analyzing Information** What were Aristotle's most significant achievements?

_____

_____

## ACTIVITY

Aristotle's writings were based on first-hand observations. Choose an
object (living or non-living) and observe it closely. Write a treatise of
your own.

Name _____ Class _____ Date _____

# Amália Rodrigues
## 1920-1999

**HOW SHE AFFECTED THE REGION**
Amália Rodrigues is known as the "Queen of the Fado," the sad folk music of Portugal. Rodrigues brought Fado music to the world through her albums, films, and countless television appearances.

*As you read the biography below,* *think about how Amália Rodrigues brought awareness of her country's poverty to the world as she followed her dream.*

The year is 1920. It is cherry blossom time in Lisbon, Portugal. But poverty is **rampant** due to the political **repression** of the time. Assassinations, war, and communism have come to the country. A poor **cobbler** who plays the trumpet is looking desperately for work. His wife gives birth to a baby girl—Amália da Piedade Rodrigues. The baby must live with her grandparents.

By age three, Rodrigues's singing talent is evident to her family and friends. Her grandfather notices that when his granddaughter sings, people stop to listen.

The government begins to limit free speech. More than 70 percent of the population is **illiterate**. When she is 14, Rodrigues gets slapped in the face for singing as she walks down the street.

Meanwhile, the "fado," a sad type of Portuguese folk song invented by the working class, became popular with the invention of radio. By 1938 Rodrigues' dream begins to take shape as she wins a local singing contest and is declared the "Queen of

### VOCABULARY
**rampant**  widespread
**repression**  the act of putting down by authority or force
**cobbler**  shoemaker
**illiterate**  unable to read or write

the Fado." A year later, she lands her first professional job as a singer. By 1949 she gains popularity in Spain, Brazil, and France. Soon after, songwriters and poets write songs just for her to perform.

In 1954 her international career takes off when she stars in her first film. Rodrigues goes on to record some 50 albums and tour throughout the world.

"The fado is not meant to be sung," she said. "It just happens." Rodrigues died in 1999, with the successful documentary *The Art of Amália* completed just a week after her death.

## WHAT DID YOU LEARN?

**1. Draw a Conclusion** How do you think poverty affected Rodrigues' determination to succeed?

_____

_____

**2. Express and Support a Point of View** Why is Rodrigues considered a legend?

_____

_____

## ACTIVITY

Write an epitaph for Amália Rodrigues. How would you capture the highlights of her life?

# Don Quixote
## by Miguel de Cervantes

**ABOUT THE READING** This excerpt is from the book *Don Quixote de La Mancha.* The main character, Don Quixote, believes he is a knight in shining armor out to save his lady. Here he battles windmills, which he thinks are terrible giants. This translation has been adapted from the original Spanish version.

**VOCABULARY**
**league** a unit of distance, approximately three miles long
**steed** horse
**lance** a spear

*As you read the passage below,* pay attention to how Cervantes uses humor to poke fun at traditions of knighthood in the Middle Ages.

"Fortune," said Don Quixote to his squire, as soon as he had seen them, "is arranging matters for us better than we could have hoped. Look there, friend Sancho Panza, where thirty or more monstrous giants rise up, all of whom I mean to engage in battle and slay, and with whose spoils we shall begin to make our fortunes. For this is righteous warfare, and it is God's good service to sweep so evil a breed from off the face of the earth."

> Sancho Panza is Don Quixote's squire, a knight in training or understudy.

"What giants?" said Sancho Panza.

"Those you see there," answered his master, "with the long arms, and some have them nearly two **leagues** long."

> Underline details that describe what Don Quixote sees and what Sancho Panza sees.

"Look, your worship," said Sancho. "What we see there are not giants but windmills, and what seem to be their arms are the vanes that turned by the wind make the millstone go."

"It is easy to see," replied Don Quixote, "that you are not used to this business of adventures. Those are giants, and if you are afraid, away with you out

Source: *Reading About the World, Volume 2,* by Paul Brians. Harcourt Brace Custom Publishing, Inc., 1999

of here and [commit] yourself to prayer, while I
engage them in fierce and unequal combat."

So saying, he gave the spur to his **steed** Rocinate,
heedless of the cries his squire Sancho sent after
him, warning him that most certainly they were
windmills and not giants he was going to attack.
He, however, was so positive they were giants that
he neither heard the cries of Sancho, nor perceived,
near as he was, what they were.

"Fly not, cowards and vile beings," he shouted,
"for a single knight attacks you."

A slight breeze at this moment sprang up, and the
great vanes began to move.

"[Although you wield] more arms than the giant
Briareus, [you] have to reckon with me!" exclaimed
Don Quixote, when he saw this.

> Briareus is a hundred-armed giant
> from Greek mythology. Epic poems
> such as the *Iliad* and the *Odyssey*
> are fantasy-adventures in which
> the hero battled many Greek gods
> and mythical creatures.

So saying, he commended himself with all his
heart to his lady Dulcinea, imploring her to support
him in such a peril. With lance braced and covered
by his shield, he charged at Rocinante's fullest gallop
and attacked the first mill that stood in front of him.
But as he drove his **lance**-point into the sail, the
wind whirled it around with such force that it
shivered the lance to pieces. It swept away with it
horse and rider, and they were sent rolling over the
plain, in sad condition indeed.

## ANALYZING LITERATURE

**1. Main Idea** How does Cervantes use humor to tell his story? Give an example.

_____

**2. Critical Thinking** What does Don Quixote's language tell you about his character?

_____

## ACTIVITY

Write a skit that uses humor and exaggeration to tell a story.

# "The Creation of Adam"
## by Michelangelo

**ABOUT THE SOURCE** The Sistine Chapel is a place of worship in the Vatican, the place where the Roman Catholic Pope lives in Vatican City in Italy. It was built between 1475 and 1483 and is one of the most famous churches in the world. The most distinguishing characteristic about the Sistine Chapel is its ceiling, painted by Renaissance artist Michelangelo. It consists of dozens of frescos, paintings done on fresh plaster. Michelangelo used bright colors, easily visible from the floor. He hung suspended from scaffolding as he painted some 300 biblical figures over a course of five years. Among the most famous of these frescos is "The Creation of Adam." The images below are details from this fresco.

*As you examine the images,* *pay close attention to the details. Recall how the Renaissance marked an increased interest in classical learning and values and the beginnings of modern science. Note how Adam is portrayed as the ideal human male with emphasis on his muscular build. Adam is clearly made in God's image, but unlike God, he appears lazy, or not quite alive.*

Source: Detail of the Creation of Adam by

Michelangelo's "The Creation of Adam", *continued*                    Primary Source

In contrast, the image of God seems to give off a certain energy. He is portrayed as all-powerful and wise, yet loving and caring.

The images illustrate human worth, love, religion, and spirituality. New studies have shown that the structure surrounding God is the exact image of a human brain. The painting reflects Michelangelo's vast knowledge of human anatomy.

Source: Creation of Adam; Detail of God and Surrounding Figures by Michelangelo, Scala/Art Resource, New York

## WHAT DID YOU LEARN?

**1.** What kind of hidden message do you think Michelangelo was trying to convey by surrounding God by an outline of the human brain?

_____

_____

_____

**2.** Adam's eyes are open, but he does not appear to "see" yet. What do you think God is intending to give Adam?

_____

_____

_____

**3.** How does this painting capture the essence of the Renaissance?

_____

_____

_____

Name _____ Class _____ Date _____

# Northern and Southern Italy

Language, religion, and family help tie together the northern and
southern regions of Italy. However, these two parts of the country also
have vast differences. Southern Italy has a weaker economy and is mainly
dependent on agriculture. While agriculture is also important in northern
Italy, this region has a much stronger economy, with major centers of
industry, trade, and tourism.

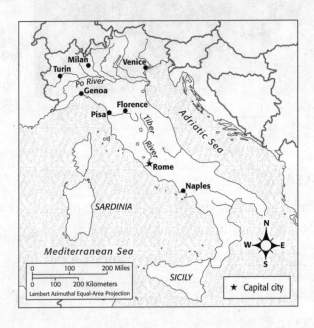

## MAP ACTIVITY

1. Draw a boundary between northern and southern Italy at the city that does not
   fully belong to either region. Label each region.

2. Highlight in a bright color the cities where industry and trade is especially
   important.

3. Highlight in a light color the cities where tourism is especially important.

4. Shade in the region known as "the breadbasket of Italy" and the region of
   southern Italy where farming is especially important.

5. Update the map key to reflect the colors you added to the map.

## ANALYZING MAPS

**1. Location**  Where are most of Italy's industrial centers located?

_____

_____

_____

**2. Place**  Which city is an important center for both industry and tourism?

_____

_____

_____

**3. Region**  Why do you think the northern part of Italy has the country's most fertile farmland?

_____

_____

_____

**4. Movement**  Over time, why do you think many cities in Italy became major centers of trade?

_____

_____

_____

**5. Human/Environment Interaction**  How does climate affect Italy's economy?

_____

_____

_____

**Southern Europe**

# Social Studies Skills
## Critical Thinking

# Reading a Climate Map

## LEARN THE SKILL

There are many different types of maps. Climate maps are an important tool in determining the average weather conditions of a place over a period of time. For example, Antarctica is known for its bitter cold and snowy conditions. Southern Europe is famous for its Mediterranean climate, which features warm, dry summers and mild, wet winters. Since weather is a powerful force of nature, it affects every aspect of life. For southern Europe, climate is one of the most valuable resources, making ideal conditions for growing crops and attracting tourists.

## PRACTICE THE SKILL

In the space below, draw a climate map of your region of the United States. Create a key with different colors that represent various climates. For example, a hot, dry climate could be shaded red, while a cold region could be shaded blue. On a separate piece of paper, write a brief description of the average weather conditions, including any seasonal changes that occur. The next time you watch a weather report on television, pay close attention to the climate maps used by the meteorologist. What colors do they use to show the current conditions where you live?

**Southern Europe**                          Geography for Life

# The Mediterranean Sea

The Mediterranean Sea has shaped the civilizations on its shores
for thousands of years. This activity explores the geography of the
Mediterranean Sea and the ways in which people have used its resources.
Read through the entire activity once. Then use an atlas to locate and
label all the places underlined below on the outline map to follow. Use
dots for the cities and draw in the rivers.

The word *Mediterranean* means "in the middle of land" or "inland"
in Latin. Europe is to its north, Asia to its east, and Africa to its south.
Twenty-one countries share the Mediterranean today. In Europe these
are Spain, France, Monaco, Italy, Malta, Slovenia, Croatia, Bosnia and
Herzegovina, Yugoslavia, Albania, and Greece. In Asia they are Turkey,
Cyprus, Syria, Lebanon, and Israel. In Africa they are Egypt, Libya,
Tunisia, Algeria, and Morocco.

## GEOGRAPHY

Covering about 1 million square miles and stretching over 2,300 miles
in length, the Mediterranean is a large body of water. Only the world's
oceans and the Arabian Sea are bigger. The Mediterranean is divided
into two basins—western and eastern—by a relatively shallow area of
the sea between Tunisia and Sicily.

These basins are further subdivided into a number of smaller seas:
the Ligurian and the Tyrrhenian Seas in the western basin and the
Adriatic, the Ionian, and the Aegean in the eastern basin.

Thousands of islands dot the Mediterranean Sea. The largest islands
are Sicily, Sardinia, Cyprus, Corsica, and Crete. Greece has the most
islands. Spain's Balearic Islands are another famous group.

Several straits have long histories of strategic importance. These
include the Strait of Gibraltar, linking the Mediterranean Sea with the
Atlantic Ocean, and the Dardenelles and Bosporus (with the Sea of
Marmara in between), linking the Mediterranean with the Black Sea.
The Strait of Messina and Strait of Otranto are other narrows in the
Mediterranean that have been used and fought over for millennia.

## TRADE

In ancient times, the great civilizations of the Mediterranean region
navigated the sea in order to trade and to establish new colonies. Places
well beyond the Mediterranean also sent their goods to the region to
be traded. In this way, various civilizations came into contact with

one another, leading to new cultural connections and innovations. In later centuries, the Mediterranean declined somewhat in commercial importance. When the Suez Canal, connecting the Red Sea with the Mediterranean, opened in 1869, it greatly enhanced the Mediterranean's role in the global transportation network.

## ENVIRONMENTAL PROBLEMS

Today the Mediterranean Sea is suffering from a number of problems. It is one of the most oil-polluted seas in the world. This pollution comes from a variety of sources, including tankers, offshore oil rigs, oil refineries and petrochemical plants, and discharge from sewers and rivers. Industrial pollutants, including heavy metals and synthetic compounds, enter the sea in many places, but are especially concentrated near the mouths of the Rhone and the Po Rivers. Much industrial activity is found in the major port cities. In Europe, these include Algeciras (on the Bay of Gibraltar), Valencia, Barcelona, Marseilles, Genoa, Venice, and Piraeus (the port city for Athens).

Runoff from the Mediterranean region's orchards, vineyards, and fields contains herbicides, pesticides, and fertilizers. Fertilizers contribute to algae blooms, which die and rot, using up the sea's oxygen. The lack of oxygen kills organisms in the water and on the seabed. The discharge and breakdown of human and animal waste have the same effect.

The Mediterranean region is also a magnet for tourists. More than 150 million visitors arrived in Spain, France, and Italy in 1998. Many of these tourists are attracted to the sun, sea, and sand of the Mediterranean. Examples of heavily developed tourist zones are the Costa Brava (North of Barcelona), the Costa Blanca (south of Valencia), and the Costa del Sol (around Malaga) in Spain and the Riviera in France, Monaco, and Italy (from Cannes to La Spezia). All those extra people put more stress on the water, air, and land of the region. The problems of pollution, inadequate water supplies, and loss of habitat and open space are worsened.

The environmental problems of the Mediterranean are being addressed by individual countries and by international organizations, including the European Union and the United Nations. Because the Mediterranean is shared by 21 different countries, international cooperation is very important for success.

# Mapping the Mediterranean

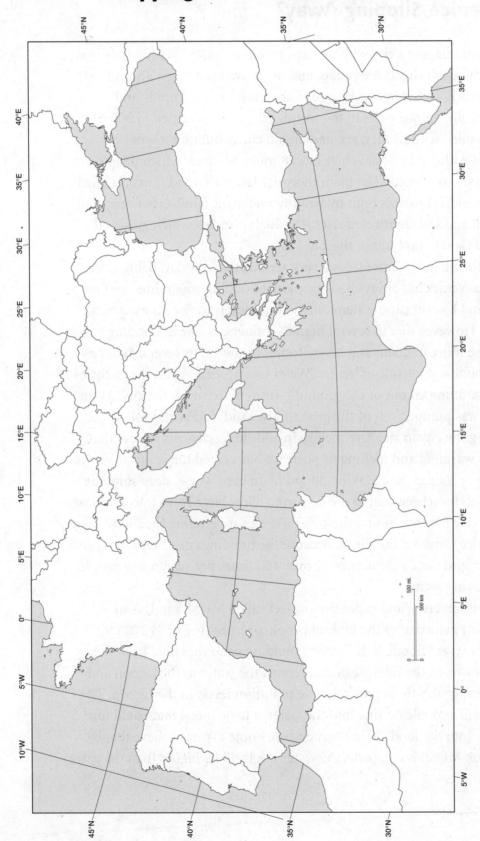

## Southern Europe

# Is Venice Slipping Away?

Can you imagine a city with no cars, trucks or buses? Venice, Italy is a city where the streets are canals, and boats are used to get around.

Venice is considered to be one of the most architecturally and historically unique cities in the world. The city was settled in 500 AD and is filled with history, art, and architecture. Built on a series of islands within a lagoon, Venice has 28 miles of canals which people use just as we use streets. The main thoroughfare, or Grand Canal, is lined with beautiful palaces built by wealthy merchant families between the twelfth and eighteenth centuries. The Rialto bridge, which crosses the Grand Canal, was built in the late 1500s.

Unfortunately, Venice faces a very serious threat today. Being close to the sea, Venice has always had occasional flooding when tides are very high and low pressure systems allow water levels to rise above typical levels. However, due to several human-influenced forces, flooding has become more frequent and severe today. In the 1950s several factories were built just outside of Venice. Water was needed to run the factories and was pumped out of the ground—from underneath the city. As the water was pumped out of the ground, the sand, rocks, and soil settled, causing the city to sink five inches. In addition, scientists believe that global warming and melting of polar ice has caused the sea near Venice to rise by four inches. Making the problem even worse, deep shipping channels have been dug in the lagoon to allow large ships to come closer to the city. The waves that these ships create are eroding the foundations of Venice's historic buildings. Because the buildings need very expensive repairs, and floods are occurring over 100 times per year, many people are moving away.

A controversial and expensive project called MOSE (an Italian acronym named after the biblical prophet Moses) began in 2003 to combat severe flooding. It involves building gates that hold back the tide. However, the tides clean and refresh the water in the lagoon and interfering with them may raise the pollution levels in the lagoon. The gates will also release zinc into the water, a toxic metal that could find its way into the food chain through fish. Some experts believe that by the time MOSE is complete, the water level will be higher than the gates can handle.

**Is Venice Slipping Away?**, *continued*                                 Critical Thinking

**1.** Do you think it is important to save Venice? Why or why not?

_____

_____

_____

**2.** List the factors that are contributing to the sinking of Venice. What factors are due to human intervention? What factors are caused by nature?

_____

_____

_____

**3.** Do you think the MOSE project is a good idea? Why or why not? What are the alternatives?

_____

_____

_____

**4.** Why is the population of Venice decreasing?

_____

_____

_____

**5.** Find Venice on the map in your book. Why do you think it was an important city for trading?

_____

_____

_____

**6.** If you were the mayor of Venice, what would you say to encourage people to stay?

_____

_____

_____

# Asking Questions

It may seem impossible to understand and remember everything that you read. Asking yourself a few simple questions as you read can help.

## CLUES TO ASKING QUESTIONS

Asking the five W's—who, what, where, when, and why—can help you find the most important information in a passage and better understand what you read.

**Who?** The answer to this question can help you identify the most important people involved in an event.

**What?** Asking this question helps you figure out what happened.

**Where?** Finding out where something happened can give you a better understanding of the event.

**When?** Knowing when an event occurred helps you relate it to other events.

**Why?** Finding the answer to this question helps you understand the causes of an event.

## ASKING QUESTIONS

Read the first paragraph under the heading The Renaissance in Section 3 of your textbook, then answer the questions below.

1. Who is this paragraph about?

2. What did the people in the passage do?

3. Where did the events described take place?

4. When did the events described take place?

5. Why did the events happen?

## EVALUATING

**Evaluating Your Skills** Did asking questions help you to better understand what you read? Use the questions below to evaluate your skills.

- Did the questions help you identify the most important information in the paragraph?

- How can asking questions help you better understand your reading?

**Southern Europe**                    Focus on Writing

# Writing a News Report

Imagine you are a newspaper reporter on special assignment in
Southern Europe. Your editor does not want you to focus on the
region's history, but rather on daily life the way it is today.

## PREWRITING

1. **Thinking about Geography** As you tour the various countries, you must keep
   track of each place's landscape, climate, and resources. Use the chart below to
   make a list for your article.

| Country | Landscape | Climate | Resources |
|---------|-----------|---------|-----------|
|         |           |         |           |
|         |           |         |           |
|         |           |         |           |
|         |           |         |           |
|         |           |         |           |

2. **Describing the Setting** Record some possible locations for the setting of your
   news report. Review Section 1 for ideas.

3. **Introducing Greece** Write down facts about Greece to include in your news
   report. What features help make Greece unique?

4. **Investigating Italy** What newsworthy events might take place in Italy? Record
   your ideas.

5. **Writing about Spain and Portugal** Review Section 4 and look for interesting
   facts about Spanish and Portuguese culture for your news report.

## WRITING

**6. Writing the Report** Follow these steps to write your news report.

- Capture your readers' attention with a vivid introduction.

- Take the reader on a written tour of each region. Use the notes you took to paint a complete picture of life in each place.

- Make sure you organize your article in a methodical way. Do not bounce from country to country. Complete one thought before moving to the next.

- Use as much detail as you can to take the reader there.

- Perhaps end your article by telling your readers why this area would be a great tourist destination. Here you might want to mention some of the historical landmarks.

## EVALUATING AND PROOFREADING

**7. Evaluating Your Report** Does your news report do a thorough, accurate job of describing life in Southern Europe? Use the questions below to evaluate and revise your news report.

- Did you describe the setting, including details about climate, landscape, and natural resources?

- Did you describe unique features found in Greece, Italy, Spain, or Portugal?

- Did you include any miscellaneous details you thought would be interesting?

**8. Proofreading Your Report** Before you send your article to your editor, check for common mistakes.

- Misspelled words, especially foreign words or places

- Double-check punctuation and grammar

Name _____ Class _____ Date _____

# Southern Europe

**BIG IDEAS**

1. The peninsulas of southern Europe have rocky terrains and sunny, mild climates.

2. The home of one of the Western world's oldest civilizations, Greece is trying to reclaim its place as a leading country in Europe.

3. Once the center of a huge empire, Italy is now one of the most prosperous countries in Europe.

4. Spain and Portugal have rich cultures, stable governments, and growing economies.

## REVIEWING VOCABULARY, TERMS, AND PLACES

In your own words, write the definition of each term.

**1.** Mediterranean climate _____

_____

**2.** contemporary _____

_____

**3.** Vatican City_____

_____

**4.** incentive _____

_____

**5.** fado _____

_____

**6.** Iberia_____

_____

**7.** Orthodox Church _____

_____

**8.** Alps _____

_____

Southern Europe, *continued*              Chapter Review

## COMPREHENSION AND CRITICAL THINKING

Read each of the following groups of sentences, and put them in sequence in the blanks provided.

**1.** ___, ___, ___, ___

    **a.** Greece forms a democracy.

    **b.** Alexander the Great conquers Greece.

    **c.** Greece becomes a monarchy.

    **d.** Greece becomes part of the Byzantine Empire.

**2.** ___, ___, ___, ___

    **a.** The Renaissance begins.

    **b.** Italy is run by an elected parliament and prime minister.

    **c.** Mussolini takes power.

    **d.** The Roman Empire collapses.

**3.** ___, ___, ___, ___

    **a.** Iberia is conquered by the Moors.

    **b.** Iberia is colonized by the Phoenicians.

    **c.** Spain and Portugal establish empires.

    **d.** Greeks established colonies on the Iberian Peninsula.

## REVIEWING THEMES

Using the lists below, determine what theme from geography they have in common.

**Themes**

| location | place | region | movement | human/environment interaction |
|---|---|---|---|---|

_____ **1.** peninsulas, Mediterranean Sea, rugged mountains

_____ **2.** philosophy, democracy, theater

_____ **3.** fertile farmland, fishing, trade

## REVIEW ACTIVITY: TRAVEL BROCHURE

You just landed a job as a tour guide for a local travel agency. You will be guiding tourists through Southern Europe. You must prepare a travel brochure for your group before they embark on their journey. You should prepare them for the climate and geography, provide some historical facts about each country, and tell them what to expect in terms of culture.

**West-Central Europe**                    Vocabulary Builder

| | | |
|---|---|---|
| Massif Central | Northern European Plain | Danube River |
| Rhine River | Jura Mountains | English Channel |
| North Sea | navigable river | |

**DIRECTIONS** On the line provided before each statement, write **T** if a statement is true and **F** if a statement is false. If the statement is false, write the correct term or terms on the line after each sentence that makes the sentence a true statement.

_____ **1.** The vast plain that stretches from the Atlantic coast into Eastern Europe is called the <u>Northern European Plain</u>.

_____

_____ **2.** The two most important rivers in West-Central Europe are the <u>Nile</u> and the <u>Mississippi</u>. Many cities and industrial areas line their banks.

_____

_____ **3.** A <u>navigable river</u> is one that is deep and wide enough for ships to use.

_____

_____ **4.** The <u>Atlantic Ocean</u> is north of Belgium and the Netherlands.

_____

_____ **5.** The <u>Danube</u> is the body of water between the North Sea and the Atlantic Ocean.

_____

**DIRECTIONS** Choose four of the vocabulary terms from the word list. On a separate sheet of paper, use these terms to write directions for how to travel (by boat, car, train, or air) from the United Kingdom to Italy.

Name _____ Class _____ Date _____

## West-Central Europe

# Vocabulary Builder

## Section 2

**DIRECTIONS** Read each sentence and fill in the blank with the word in the word pair that best completes the sentence.

1. _____ is a style of painting developed by French artists that uses rippling light to create an impression of a scene. (**Impressionism/Abstract expressionism**)

2. _____ is the capital of France. (**London/Paris**)

3. The Dutch use _____, or earthen walls, in addition to dams and pumps to hold back the sea. (**dikes/trenches**)

4. Brussels, the capital of Belgium, is considered a _____ city because of its many foreign influences. (**cosmopolitan/sprawling**)

5. _____ is the capital of the Netherlands. (**Amsterdam/The Hague**)

**DIRECTIONS** Write a word or short phrase that has the same meaning as the term given.

6. *joie de vivre* _____

7. Marseille _____

8. The Hague _____

9. Brussels _____

10. Benelux _____

Europe and Russia

**West-Central Europe**

Vocabulary Builder

| Berlin | chancellor | cantons | purpose |
|--------|-----------|---------|---------|
| Vienna | neutral | Bern | |

**DIRECTIONS** Read each sentence and fill in the blank with the word in the word pair that best completes the sentence.

1. _____ is the capital of Germany. (**Vienna/Berlin**)

2. In Germany, a parliament elects a _____, or prime minister, who runs the government. (**canton/chancellor**)

3. Switzerland is made up of 26 districts called _____. (**cantons/Bern**)

4. _____ is the capital of Austria and also its largest city. (**Berlin/Vienna**)

5. The capital of Switzerland, _____, is centrally located between the country's German- and French-speaking regions. (**Bern/Vienna**)

**DIRECTIONS** Choose five terms from the word bank. Use these terms to write a summary of what you learned in this section.

_____

_____

_____

_____

_____

_____

_____

_____

_____

_____

Europe and Russia

# Jacques-Yves Cousteau

1910–1997

**HOW HE AFFECTED THE WORLD** Jacques
Cousteau was an underwater explorer,
inventor, filmmaker, and **environmentalist**.
Through documentary films shown on
television in the 1960s and 1970s, he
introduced millions of people to the
mysterious power of the ocean.

Bettmann/CORBIS

*As you read the biography below, think about
how Cousteau's courageous underwater exploration and innovative filmmaking helped people
understand the ocean and become aware of dangers to the environment.*

**VOCABULARY**

**environmentalist** a person
working to solve
environmental problems

**apparatus** instruments or
tools needed for a specific
use

**excursion** a round-trip
journey

**W**hat if you went swimming one day—and it
changed your life? For Jacques-Yves Cousteau, a
simple swim opened up a whole new world of
possibility and adventure.

In the early 1930s, Cousteau was training to be a
pilot with the French Navy until a serious car accident ended his studies. However, in 1936, Cousteau
went swimming one day with goggles. For the first
time, he was able to see the wonders of underwater
life. Without knowing it at the time, he had discovered his new career.

Cousteau's experience in the Navy allowed him
to further research and explore the ocean—and to
invent devices that helped his work. To help divers
stay underwater longer, Cousteau helped invent
an early form of diving equipment called the
Self-Contained Underwater Breathing **Apparatus**,
or SCUBA, in 1943.

In 1950, Cousteau bought a used, 400-ton ship
and turned it into a laboratory filled with

diving and research equipment. He named the
ship *Calypso*. Cousteau used the ship to explore
oceans and other bodies of water all over the world.
Cousteau documented his underwater **excursions**
and turned his discoveries into more than 50 books
and 115 films.

Cousteau's films exposed viewers to the unseen
beauty of underwater life. They also uncovered the
harmful effects of pollution and other environmental problems. His films won him loyal fans and
three Academy Awards. His environmental efforts
also earned him recognition. In 1977, Cousteau
was awarded the United Nations International
Environmental Prize.

To further promote environmentalism and
protect ocean life, Cousteau started a nonprofit
organization called The Cousteau Society in 1974.
The organization now has about 300,000 members
worldwide.

## WHAT DID YOU LEARN?

**1. Identify** How did Cousteau contribute to the environmental movement?

_____

_____

**2. Expressing and Supporting a Point of View** Do you think that Cousteau's films
are important to the field of science? Provide reasons or examples to support your
point of view.

_____

_____

## ACTIVITY

Do research to find pictures of different aspects of ocean life, such as
sharks, whales, or plants. Using your pictures, create a collage about
ocean life. Present your collage to the class.

# EMMY NOETHER
## 1882–1935

**HOW SHE AFFECTED THE WORLD**
Until Emmy Noether, only men had been leading mathematicians. Noether's work in Germany in the early 1900s led to significant advances in math and physics. She even influenced Albert Einstein.

© Photo Researchers, Inc.

*As you read the biography below,* think about how Emmy Noether's determination helped her overcome obstacles to have a career in mathematics.

*"In the realm of algebra, in which the most gifted mathematicians have been busy for centuries, she discovered methods that have proved of enormous importance. . ."* – Albert Einstein, in a tribute to Emmy Noether

W hat if your father was a math teacher but you could not enroll at his school—because of your gender? Emmy Noether faced this problem.

Noether's father was a well-known mathematician in Germany. In 1900, when she was 18, Noether decided to study mathematics at the university level. She studied at the school where her father taught math. However, because Noether was a woman, the university did not allow her to enroll in classes for credit. **Auditing** classes was her only option.

After Noether audited classes for two years, she passed a test that allowed her to study math at the **doctorate** level. In 1907, after five years of study, Noether earned her doctorate in mathematics and was ready to teach.

**VOCABULARY**

**auditing** attending a college class without receiving credit

**doctorate** one of the highest academic degrees from a university

**theorem** a statement in math that has been figured out from other statements

Despite her talent, the university she had graduated from would not hire female professors. Instead, she helped her father with research. She also occasionally substituted for him when he was sick.

Noether's work began to get attention from other mathematicians. Universities asked her to lecture at their schools—without pay. Two **theorems** she proved in 1918 turned out to be very important to Albert Einstein's research in physics. Eventually she began to receive pay for her work as a mathematician, but it was less than what men were making.

Noether, whose family was Jewish, left Germany in 1933 when the Nazis rose to power. She came to the United States and began teaching math at Bryn Mawr College near Philadephia. At Bryn Mawr, Emmy was finally able to earn equal pay for her work. However, her new life in the United States was short lived. She died from complications following surgery in 1935.

## WHAT DID YOU LEARN?

**1. Recall** Why was Emmy Noether denied the chance to earn credits at her father's university?

_____

_____

**2. Expressing and Supporting a Point of View** Besides contributing to mathematics, what do you think Noether contributed to society by pursuing an academic career? Provide reasons to support your point of view.

_____

_____

## ACTIVITY

Do research to find out more about what mathematicians do. Write a job description for a mathematician, listing necessary tools and tasks of the job.

# The Lily of the Valley
## by Honoré de Balzac

**ABOUT THE READING** This excerpt is from the novel, *The Lily of the Valley*. French author Honoré de Balzac explores the intense friendship between a young man, Félix, and a married woman, Madame de Mortsauf. In this excerpt, Félix poetically describes his nature walks while visiting Madame de Mortsauf's family in the country in the early 1800s.

## VOCABULARY

**botanist** a person who studies plant life

**osprey** a large hawk whose back is mostly dark brown and whose stomach is mostly white

**fallowland** a pale, open field

**torrent** a violent surge or rush, often used to describe water

**confounding** confusing

*As you read the passage below,* pay attention to Félix's observations about nature and his awareness of his environment.

Twice a week, for the rest of my stay at Frapesle, I repeated the lengthy labors of this poetic creation, for which were needed all the varieties of greenery. Of these plants I made a thorough study, less as a **botanist** than as a poet, examining them for their spirit rather than their form. To reach the place where a certain flower grew, I often covered enormous distances, to the edge of lakes, into valleys, up on to high rocks and into open heathland, finding a prized sprig . . . deep in the wood or hidden among bracken. I found, during these trips, my own initiation into pleasures unknown to the scholar in his world of thought, to the farmer busy with his marketable produce, to the artisan glued to the city, or to the tradesman chained to his counter, pleasures known to a few foresters, a few woodsmen, a few dreamers. There are to be found, in nature, effects of limitless significance, which rise to the level of the greatest moral concepts. A clump

> Bracken is a kind of large, leafy plant.

From *The Lily of the Valley* by Honoré de Balzac, translated by Lucienne Hill. Copyright © by **Carroll & Graf Publishers, Inc.** Reproduced by permission of the publisher.

of heather in bloom, perhaps, covered in diamonds
of dew with sunlight dancing on them . . .
Or a patch of woodland, ringed with crumbling
rocks, streaked with sand, clad in moss and decked
with junipers, which makes you catch your breath
at the savage, jarring, fearfulness of it, as the shriek
of the **osprey** breaks the silence . . . Then, outside
those cool, leafy woods a stretch of chalky **fallowland**, where, over hot, crackling mosses grass snakes
slither homeward . . . their slender, elegant heads
held high. Fling over these scenes, now **torrents** of
sunshine streaming down like nourishing waves,
now grey banks of clouds aligned like furrows on an
old man's brow, now the cold tones of a sky weakly
tinged with orange and streaked with pale blue
bands. Then listen: you will hear . . . harmonies in
the midst of a **confounding** silence.

> The author is describing the beauty he sees on his nature walks by comparing it to objects and wildlife in nature.

> A furrow is a deep wrinkle.

## ANALYZING LITERATURE

**1. Main Idea** According to the passage, what is Félix's "poetic creation"?

_____

_____

**2. Critical Thinking: Analyzing** How aware is Félix of his environment? Use
examples to support your answer.

_____

_____

## ACTIVITY

Do research to find images of Paris, the French Alps, or the French
Riviera. Imagine that you are describing the images to someone who
has never seen them. Describe each image in detail.

# "Above the Clouds, the French Glimpse the Old Grandeur"

## by Elaine Sciolino

**ABOUT THE READING** In December, 2004, the Millau Bridge opened near Millau, a small city in the Massif Central region of southern France. In this newspaper article from *The New York Times,* journalist Elaine Sciolino describes the bridge—the world's tallest—and explains why it is so unusual.

**VOCABULARY**

**audacious** daring

**foreman** person in charge of a group of workers

**transparent** clear

**aerodynamic** designed with rounded edges to reduce the effects of wind

**pylon** tower for support-ing wires

*As you read* note how the article connects the bridge to the physical geography of the region.

MILLAU, France—Higher than the Eiffel Tower, longer than the <u>Champs-Élysées</u>, the Millau Bridge is a triumph of engineering, imagination, and will.

> The Champs-Élysées is a wide, tree-lined street that runs through the center of Paris. It contains many cafes, theaters, and shops.

For President Jacques Chirac, the soaring butterfly of steel and concrete that spans the <u>Tarn Valley</u> is nothing less than an "**audacious**" work of art and a symbol of "a modern and conquering France."

> The Tarn Valley is a deep river valley in the Massif Central region.

No matter that the man who designed the bridge, the world's highest, is Norman Foster . . . perhaps Britain's most famous . . . architect . . .

"This is a work that touches all of us," said Thomas Ercker, a **foreman** who worked on the project for more than two years. "There is only one time in your life you can do something like this. I am convinced that we've created a jewel. I have goose bumps all over."

. . . Slender, graceful, even fragile-looking, the gently-curving bridge was built in only three years, the product of computer design technology, global satellite positioning, and lighter, high-tech materials that shortened the timetable and cut costs.

The deck for the four-lane road is made from a new high grade of steel instead of concrete. **Transparent aerodynamic** windscreens protect vehicles from high winds and let travelers savor the rugged landscape.

The pale color of the construction allows it to blend with the sky, giving it a transparent feel. At its highest point—1,125 feet from the bottom of the valley to the top of the **pylon** atop the tallest pillar—the bridge is more than 50 feet higher than the Eiffel Tower.

> The Eiffel Tower is a 1,063 ft tall metal tower in Paris. It was the tallest building in the world until 1930.

"It had to be very light, very delicate, but immensely strong," said [Foster] . . . "The driving experience is close to flying. The trip across the valley is like that of a bird." . . .

## WHAT DID YOU LEARN?

**1.** How is the Millau Bridge different from other bridges?

_____

_____

**2.** Based on the description in the article, what do you think bridge foreman Thomas Ercker means when he says, "I am convinced that we have created a jewel?"

_____

_____

**3.** How does driving across the Millau Bridge connect people with the physical geography of the Massif Central region?

_____

_____

Geography and History

# Countries in the European Union

The European Union (EU) was formed to promote peace between
European countries by uniting them politically and economically. The
EU now consists of 25 countries. The EU allows Europeans more free-
dom to work, live, trade, study, and travel within Europe.

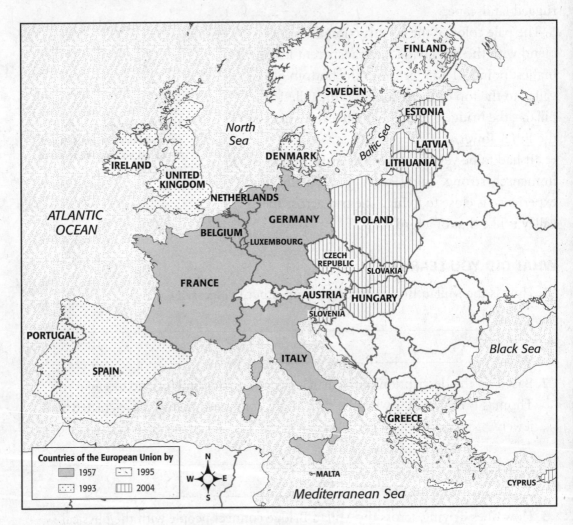

## MAP ACTIVITY

Use the European Union map from your textbook or an atlas to help
you complete this activity.

1. Use a bright color to write the names of countries that became members of the
   EU by 1957.

2. Use a different bright color to write the names of countries that became members
   of the EU after 1957 and by 1995.

**3.** Use a third color to write the names of countries that became members of the EU after 1995 and by 2004.

**4.** Use the map legend to reflect the colors you used on the map.

## INTERPRETING MAPS

**1. Region** List the countries that were members of the European Union by 1957.

_____

_____

**2. Location** Which three European countries are islands?

_____

_____

**3. Place** Which of the countries that became members of the European Union between 1995 and 2004 is the largest?

_____

_____

**4. Location** What country is bordered by Germany, Belgium, and France?

_____

_____

**5. Critical Thinking: Analyzing** Do you think the European Union has benefited Europeans? Use examples to support your answer.

_____

_____

**West-Central Europe**

# Social Studies Skills

## Chart and Graph

# Analyzing a Circle Graph

## LEARN THE SKILL

Analyzing circle graphs can help you to understand how different parts make up a whole. As you analyze the circle graph below, check the title to see the graph's subject and purpose. Use the labels in the "pie slice" to tell what is being represented. Finally, analyze the data by comparing the size of the slices in the graph.

## PRACTICE THE SKILL

Analyze the circle graph and answer the questions that follow.

**Land Use in Belgium**

Other uses
76%

Arable land
23.5%

Permanent
crops
0.5%

1. What percentage of Belgium's land is arable, or land that can be used to grow crops that are replanted after each harvest?

_____

2. What percentage of Belgium's land is available for permanent crops, or land that can be cultivated for crops that are not replanted after each harvest?

_____

3. What percentage of Belgium's land is used for something other than crops?

_____

4. What part of the circle graph makes up less than 1% of the total circle?

_____

Europe and Russia

# The EU and NATO: Past, Present, and Future

After World War II, the economy of every European country was in ruins. Some European leaders realized that Europe had a better chance of restoring its economic health if countries worked together and opened their markets to one another rather than remaining isolated. These leaders hoped that with free trade and cooperation, Europe would be able to create an economy that could compete successfully with the world's two new superpowers, the United States and the Soviet Union. Furthermore, this economic cooperation would reduce the chance of future conflicts within Europe.

On January 1, 1958, the European Economic Community (EEC) came into being. It was formed by Belgium, the Netherlands, Luxembourg, Germany, France, and Italy. The coming together of Germany and France was particularly significant after several centuries of conflict. The countries that formed the EEC dedicated themselves to the creation of a common market and the removal of trade barriers.

At first, Great Britain decided to stay out of the EEC. It was still committed to the economic arrangements it had with members of the British Commonwealth. Britain attempted to join the EEC in the 1960s, but its entry was vetoed twice by France, a long-standing rival. Britain was finally admitted in 1973, along with two countries that have strong trade ties to it, Ireland and Denmark. By this time, the EEC had become the EC (European Community).

In 1981 Greece was approved as a member of the EC, and in 1986 Spain and Portugal followed. These three countries were poorer than the others (together with Ireland, they were sometimes called "the poor four"). Special arrangements were made for these new countries, so that they could join but not have their own economies immediately over-whelmed by the more efficient economies of the older EC members.

In 1993 the EC became the EU (European Union). This new name reflected the greater ambitions of the organization. The EU wanted to have a completely integrated economy. This integration included the free movement of goods, services, capital, and people and the creation of a common currency (the euro). It also meant more agreement on political, social, and even defense matters. Some people used the term "United States of Europe" to suggest how closely tied the countries of the EU might become.

In 1995 Austria, Finland, and Sweden joined the EU. All of these countries are prosperous democracies. Even before joining, they did much of their trading with EU countries and worked closely with the EU on many issues.

Today there are 25 members of the EU. Cyprus, Czech Republic, Estonia, Hungary, Latvia, Lithuania, Malta, Poland, Slovakia, and Slovenia became members on May 1, 2004. With the exception of Malta and Cyprus, these countries recently had communist governments and centrally planned economies. They were satellite states of the Soviet Union until its collapse in the 1990s. Bulgaria and Romania are expected to become members in 2007.

A second important international organization with a European focus is the North Atlantic Treaty Organization (NATO). This military alliance was created in 1949 by a group of countries committed to each other's defense: Belgium, Canada, Denmark, France, Iceland, Italy, Luxembourg, the Netherlands, Norway, Portugal, the United Kingdom, and the United States. In 1952 Greece and Turkey joined; in 1955, Germany; in 1982, Spain. An expansion of NATO occurred in 1999, when former Soviet allies Poland, Hungary, and the Czech Republic joined NATO. Bulgaria, Estonia, Latvia, Lithuania, Romania, Slovakia, and Slovenia joined NATO in 2004. With the Soviet Union gone and the Cold War over, NATO has turned some of its energies to peacekeeping efforts, a role it played in the Balkan troubles.

## YOU ARE THE GEOGRAPHER

In this exercise, you will construct a map showing the growth of these important international organizations. Use the map on the next page to show the growth of the EU and of NATO.

1. Use an atlas or your textbook to correctly label all the countries mentioned in the above discussion.

2. Use colored pencils or felt pens to color the EU countries as follows: the six original members (1957)—green; the next 3 (1973)—blue; Greece (1981)—purple; Spain and Portugal (1986)—orange; Austria, Sweden, and Finland (1995)—yellow. Color the 10 countries that became members in 2004 in red stripes.

Europe and Russia

**3.** Use a black pen to indicate the NATO countries as follows: put horizontal stripes across the 12 original members; put vertical stripes down the 4 members that joined between 1952 and 1982; put diagonal stripes on the 3 that joined in 1999; put dots on the 7 counties that joined in 2004.

**4.** Put a title on your map and make a key for it.

**5.** Notice that Iceland and Norway are not members of or applicants to the EU. Notice that Sweden, Finland, Ireland, and Austria are not members of NATO. Switzerland, Albania, and most of the countries that used to be part of Yugoslavia are both non-EU and non-NATO countries. Have different people in your group find out why one of these countries has not joined these organizations. (For example, Iceland worries about other countries being able to fish in its waters if it joins the EU.) Other students could find out what are the challenges that applicants have to meet to become members of the EU. Share your findings.

**West-Central Europe**                                      Critical Thinking

# A Taste of France

*The term for elaborately prepared high-class food is haute cuisine (oht*
*kwih ZEEN). It is appropriate that the term is French, because France is*
*well known for its fine foods and styles of cooking. To learn about haute*
*cuisine and its origins, study the following information and answer the*
*questions.*

   *Haute cuisine* grew out of regional French cookery. It was created
in country kitchens through the ages. Basic roads and no system of
transportation meant that food had to be grown easily and locally.
Geography dictated the ingredients of the dishes.

### WHAT GROWS WHERE?

In a region where pastures are good—such as Poitou-Charentes, across
the north and down into Burgundy and Franché-Comté—cattle are
raised. Cattle produce butter, an important ingredient in local dishes.
The Vosges mountains and the Alps provide good grassland in high
summer, so dairy foods are abundant there are as well. A temperate
climate encourages the growing of fruit and vegetables.

   The stony land of Provence and the hot harsh landscapes stretching
west across the Rhône into Languedoc-Roussillon do not favor cattle
rearing. So the main source of meat and cheese in these areas was goats.
The olive tree thrives in this region's harsh soil, and its oil became the
mainstay of southern kitchens. Herbs, tomatoes, peppers, garlic, and
citrus fruits—all of which need heat to grow—have also added their
flavors to this region's cooking.

### FRUITS OF THE FOREST

Much of central and southwest France is covered by deep forests or wild
uplands. Traditional crops of other parts of France cannot be grown
here. Chestnut or corn flour is often substituted for wheat. Pigs and
geese are raised instead of cattle, and their flavor is present in many of
this region's dishes. The lentils and beans (fresh or dried) that also grow
here are perfect for counterbalancing the richness of these meats.

   In the far southwest, the Basques have the widest choice of cuisine
styles. The fertile land and temperate climate mean that almost
everything will grow here. Game, in the country's extensive woodlands,
provides extra protein, as does seafood. The Atlantic Ocean teems with
seafood of all kinds: there are tunny, sardines, and anchovies in the

Mediterranean. Great salmon, eels, and freshwater crayfish come from France's many rivers.

## NOT A THING IS WASTED

"Waste not" has always been the French cook's motto. As with the pig ("everything used but the squeak"), nothing pulled from the sea, lake, or river is thrown away. If a fish is too small or bony to be served in the usual way, it is still excellent for soups or stews. Most famous of all is bouillabaisse, a soup made from spiny rockfish, tiny crabs, and crayfish and other shellfish from the Mediterranean.

Use maps from your textbook and an atlas to help answer these questions.

**1.** How did geography influence the development of French cooking? How many types of traditional regional cooking does the passage identify?

_____

_____

**2.** What type of traditional cuisine would you expect to find in the Massif Central?

_____

_____

**3.** Would *bouillabaisse* be more typical of Marseilles or of Paris? Explain why.

_____

**4.** Would the food of Bordeaux be more like that of Toulouse or of Reims? Explain why.

_____

_____

**5.** Describe how the cuisine of Nice would differ from the traditional foods of Tours.

_____

_____

## West-Central Europe

# Recognizing Word Origins

Many of the words we use today come from other languages, such as Latin, French, and German. Knowing the origin of a word can help you understand its meaning. If you come across an unfamiliar word, or if a word sounds foreign, think about where it may have originated. If you are unsure of a word's origin, look up the word in the dictionary. Discovering the origin of a word may also help you begin to learn another language.

## SECTION 1: PHYSICAL GEOGRAPHY

Many physical features are given names. Some of the names have foreign origins. Reread the text and the maps in Section 1. Find names that have a foreign origin. Write the word, the meaning, and the origin in the space below.

_____

_____

_____

_____

## SECTION 2: FRANCE AND THE BENELUX COUNTRIES

Several foreign words appear in Section 2. Reread the section to help you answer the questions below. Your answers will help you learn more about word origins.

**1.** What French art movement has a Latin root in its name?

_____

**2.** What French word means "enjoyment of life"?

_____

**3.** What French word is often used in the United States to mean "coffee house"?

_____

**4.** What does the word *Netherlands* mean?

_____

_____

## SECTION 3: GERMANY AND THE ALPINE COUNTRIES

Many German customs have made their way to the United States, such
as the Christmas tree. Reread Section 3 and find German words that
have made it into American culture. Some words may be names of customs, events, or companies. Make your list below.

_____

_____

_____

_____

_____

## RECOGNIZING LATIN ROOTS

Are there any words in the chapter that have Latin roots? Write down a
word with Latin roots from each section on the lines below. Then write
the definition of these words.

**1. Word for Section 1:**_____

    Definition:_____

    _____

**2. Word for Section 2:**_____

    Definition:_____

    _____

**3. Word for Section 3:**_____

    Definition:_____

    _____

**West-Central Europe**                    Focus on Speaking

# Presenting a Persuasive Speech

Issues are topics that people disagree about. As you read the chapter, think about which issues seem important to you. Then write and present a persuasive speech in which you take a stand on one of these issues.

## PREWRITING

1. **Noting the Physical Geography** Think about which issues in the section are related to land use and natural resources. List the issues below or on a separate chart.

| Land Use/Natural Resource Issues |
|---|
| *Does coal mining in the Central Uplands damage the environment?* |
| *Does importing fuel into West-Central Europe help or hurt the region's economy?* |
| |

2. **Describing France and the Benelux Countries** Think about one possible issue for each country described in the section. List the issues below or on a separate chart.

| Country | Possible Issue |
|---|---|
| Belgium | *Should all Belgians have to speak the same language?* |
| France | |
| Luxembourg | |
| The Netherlands | |

**3. Describing Germany and the Alpine Countries** Think about one possible issue for each country described in the section. List the issues below or on a separate chart.

| Country | Possible Issue |
|---|---|
| Switzerland | *The Swiss Alps are the loveliest area in West-Central Europe.* |
| Austria | |
| Germany | |

## SPEAKING

**4. Presenting a Persuasive Speech** Choose one of the issues you identified. Write an opinion statement about your issue. List three facts or examples that support your opinion. Use the chapter and other sources to find information. Use your lists to write your persuasive speech. Practice delivering your speech in a confident tone of voice. Use the model below to get started.

> *Why the Dutch Polders Should Be Restored to Wetlands*
> *The Dutch polders should be restored to wetlands because . . .*

## EVALUATING AND PROOFREADING

**5. Evaluating Your Speech** Is your speech persuasive enough to make people change their minds about an issue? Use the questions below to evaluate and revise your speech.

**Rubric**

- Does your speech explain why the issue is important?

- Does your speech identify both sides of the issue? Does it explain why your position is best?

- Does your speech clearly explain your stand on the issue?

- Is your speech as a whole persuasive and interesting?

**6. Proofreading Your Speech** Check the following:

- capitalization and spelling of all proper names and places

- punctuation, grammar, and spelling

**West-Central Europe**                    Chapter Review

**BIG IDEAS**

1. West-Central Europe has a range of landscapes, a mild climate, and rich farmland.

2. France and the Benelux countries have strong economies and rich cultural traditions.

3. Germany and the Alpine Countries are prosperous countries with similar cultures.

## REVIEWING VOCABULARY, TERMS, AND PLACES

Using the clues provided, fill in the letter blanks with the correct term.

**1.** a river that is deep and wide enough for ships to use

__ __ __ __ __ __ __ __ __ __

**2.** a style of painting that uses rippling light to create an impression of a scene

__ __ __ __ __ __ __ __ __ __ __ __ __ __

**3.** the capital of France

__ __ __ __ __

**4.** earthen walls, dams, and pumps to hold back the sea

__ __ __ __ __ __

**5.** the capital of Belgium

__ __ __ __ __ __ __ __

**6.** the reason something is done

__ __ __ __ __ __ __

**7.** a German prime minister

__ __ __ __ __ __ __ __ __ __

**8.** unbiased

__ __ __ __ __ __ __

**West-Central Europe,** *continued*                              Chapter Review

## COMPREHENSION AND CRITICAL THINKING

Read the **FALSE** statement below. On the line provided, replace the underlined word or words to make this statement **TRUE**.

**1.** In France, the uplands include the Jura Mountains and the <u>Rhine</u>.

_____

**2.** <u>The Hague</u> is the capital of the Netherlands.

_____

**3.** <u>Germany</u> has been neutral for hundreds of years.

_____

## REVIEWING THEMES

In the space provided, explain how each term relates to the theme listed below.

**Theme:** *movement*

**1.** navigable river

_____

_____

**2.** European Union

_____

_____

**3.** Berlin Wall

_____

_____

## REVIEW ACTIVITY: TIME LINE

On a large piece of poster board, create a time line that gives an overview of the main political, cultural, and social events that took place in one of the following countries: France, the Netherlands, Belgium, Luxembourg, Germany, Austria, or Switzerland. Try to find visuals that represent the various events. Place them in the appropriate spots on the time line.

**Northern Europe**

Vocabulary Builder

| | | |
|---|---|---|
| Arctic Circle | British Isles | fjord |
| geothermal energy | glaciers | hydroelectric energy |
| North Atlantic Drift | peninsula | Scandinavia |
| subarctic | tundra | volcanoes |

**DIRECTIONS** Read each sentence and fill in the blank with the word in the word pair that best completes each sentence.

1. Many lakes in the British Isles were carved by _____ millions of years ago. (**volcanoes/glaciers**)

2. Northern Europe is made up of the British Isles and _____. (**Scandinavia/the Artic Circle**)

3. A _____ is a narrow inlet of the sea set between high, rocky cliffs. (**fjord/peninsula**)

4. Energy produced from the heat of Earth's interior is called

_____. (**geothermal energy/hydroelectric energy**)

5. Northern Europe experiences a mild climate due to the
_____. (**Arctic Circle/North Atlantic Drift**)

**DIRECTIONS** Look at each set of four vocabulary terms. On the line provided, write the letter of the term that does not relate to the others.

_____ **6. a.** glacier
       **b.** rainfall
       **c.** fjord
       **d.** cliff

_____ **8. a.** Ireland
       **b.** England
       **c.** Scotland
       **d.** Denmark

_____ **7. a.** tundra
       **b.** soil
       **c.** forest
       **d.** ocean

_____ **9. a.** North Atlantic Drift
       **b.** mild climate
       **c.** ocean current
       **d.** subarctic climate

Europe and Russia

| | | |
|---|---|---|
| agreement | constitutional monarchy | disarm |
| Dublin | Industrial Revolution | London |
| Magna Carta | Stonehenge | |

**DIRECTIONS** Read each sentence and fill in the blank with the word in the word pair that best completes the sentence.

1. The _____ was characterized by the growth of industries like textiles, iron, and steel. (**Industrial Revolution/Magna Carta**)

2. An _____ led to the creation of a national assembly and a cease fire in Northern Ireland in the late 1990s. (**agreement/Industrial Revolution**)

3. _____ is an ancient monument in the British Isles that was built 5,000 years ago. (**Dublin/Stonehenge**)

4. A _____ is a government that has a monarch and a legislative body that makes the laws. (**Magna Carta/constitutional monarchy**)

5. Peace talks in Northern Ireland were stalled when some groups refused to

_____. (**disarm/agreement**)

**DIRECTIONS** Write three words or phrases that describe the term.

6. London _____

7. Dublin _____

8. Magna Carta _____

# Northern Europe

**Vocabulary Builder**

**Section 3**

| | | |
|---|---|---|
| domination | geysers | Helsinki |
| hot springs | neutral | Oslo |
| Stockholm | uninhabitable | Vikings |

**DIRECTIONS** Answer each question by writing a sentence that contains at least one word from the word bank.

**1.** How were longboats used by Scandinavian warriors?

_____

_____

**2.** Why do most people in Greenland live on the southwest coast?

_____

_____

**3.** What role did Sweden play in World War I and World War II?

_____

_____

**4.** How are many homes in Iceland heated?

_____

_____

**5.** What city in Scandinavia is often called a floating city and why?

_____

_____

Europe and Russia

# Mary, Queen of Scots
## 1542–1587

**HOW SHE AFFECTED THE WORLD** Mary, Queen of Scots is Scotland's most famous queen, known for her beauty and charm. She was a successful ruler for a time. Eventually, she was forced out of Scotland and beheaded in England at the age of 44.

*As you read the biography below,* think about how likeable Mary must have been to win over the Scottish people.

Mary Stuart was only six days old when her father died, making her Queen of Scotland. At age five, Mary's mother, a Frenchwoman, sent her to France to be brought up at the court of King Henry II. At that time, she was **betrothed** to the heir to the French throne.

During her time in France, Mary became a true **Renaissance** princess, educated in several languages, music, and poetry. She also loved outdoor activities such as golf, archery, and hunting. Through her marriage to Francis II in 1558, Mary actually became the queen of France. It was short-lived, however, as Francis died in 1560.

Mary returned to Scotland the next year, only to find that she was a Catholic queen in a Protestant country. Because of her French education and manners, Scottish people thought of her as a Frenchwoman. Despite these challenges, she won the people over and ruled successfully for a time.

Mary's downfall started with her marriage to her English cousin, Lord Darnley, in 1565. Lord Darnley was unpopular with the people. Royal counselors advised Mary to get rid of him. In 1567 Darnley

**VOCABULARY**

**betrothed** arranged to marry

**Renaissance** period of cultural, scientific, and artistic change in European history

**treason** act of betraying one's country

was murdered. A few months later, Mary married the prime suspect. This made her unpopular with the Scots, and in 1567, she was imprisoned and forced to give up the throne to her infant son, James. In 1568, she fled to England.

Queen Elizabeth I, a cousin of Mary's, kept Mary imprisoned in England rather than turning her over to the Scottish government. Over the next 18 years, Mary tried unsuccessfully to escape. Mary was also linked to many plots to overthrow or kill Queen Elizabeth, as her family lineage gave her a claim to the English throne. Tired of the constant threat, Elizabeth eventually had her cousin tried for **treason.** Mary was beheaded in 1587.

## WHAT DID YOU LEARN?

**1. Analyze and Make Judgments** How did Mary's choice in husbands affect her life?

_____

_____

**2. Drawing Conclusions** Why do you think Mary may have plotted against Queen Elizabeth?

_____

_____

## ACTIVITY

Conduct additional research about Mary Stuart's life, and create a detailed family tree to show how she was related to other rulers of the time.

# Hans Christian Andersen
## 1805–1875

**HOW HE AFFECTED THE WORLD** Hans Christian Andersen is Denmark's most famous author. His fairy tales have been read and loved by adults and children around the world since his first collection appeared in 1835. Many of his stories, which include "The Ugly Duckling" and "The Princess and the Pea," are autobiographical.

*As you read the biography below,* think about the perseverance that helped Andersen become so successful and famous.

Hans Christian Andersen's own life was much like one of his fairy tales. He was born in Odense, Denmark, the son of a poor shoemaker who died when Andersen was eleven. His grandfather was known as a **mad eccentric**. His grandmother worked in the local insane asylum and occasionally allowed Andersen to go to work with her. Near the asylum, the poor townswomen spun thread. Andersen explained, "I often went in there and was very soon a favorite . . . I passed for a remarkably wise child, that would not live long; and they rewarded my **eloquence** by telling me tales in return; and thus a world as rich as that of the *Thousand and One Nights* was revealed to me."

　Andersen went to Copenhagen at the age of 14 in hopes of becoming a famous actor. Although that plan failed, he met Jonas Collin, who was associated with the Royal Theatre. Collin took Anderson under his wing and secured a royal grant for him to continue his education.

## VOCABULARY

**autobiographical** written by a writer about him- or herself

**mad** insane

**eccentric** someone thought to be odd or strange

**eloquence** ability to express oneself well

***Thousand and One Nights*** a very old collection of Arabic stories (also called *Arabian Nights*)

He was admitted to the University of Copenhagen in 1828. The next year, he published his first important literary work, *A Journey on Foot from Holmen's Canal to the Eastern Point of Amager.* This fantastic tale was an instant success.

Andersen then turned to playwriting and poetry, but was mostly known as a novelist. In 1835, he published his first book of fairy tales, *Eventyr.* (In Dutch, an *eventyr* is a kind of fantastic tale, not solely intended for children.)

While some of Andersen's tales end happily, many are tragic and pessimistic. He wrote 156 fairy tales in all. Some of his most widely recognized stories include "The Ugly Duckling," "The Princess and the Pea," "The Snow Queen," and "The Emperor's New Clothes."

## WHAT DID YOU LEARN?

1. **Analyze and Make Judgments**  How did Hans Christian Andersen's move to Copenhagen affect his life?

_____

_____

2. **Using Deductive Reasoning**  How was Hans Christian Andersen's own life similar to a fairy tale?

_____

_____

## ACTIVITY

Conduct additional research on the life of Hans Christian Andersen. Then find one of his fairy tales that is autobiographical. Pretend you are a Danish newspaper reporter interviewing Andersen about the connection between his life and this fairy tale. Write your interview on a separate piece of paper.

# Romeo and Juliet
## by William Shakespeare

> **ABOUT THE READING** William Shakespeare is often considered the most important playwright in the history of British literature. He was also an actor and poet. Shakespeare's plays are divided into comedies, histories, and tragedies. *Romeo and Juliet* is one of his most famous tragedies. His plays and **sonnets** are written in **iambic pentameter**.

### VOCABULARY

**sonnet** a poem with fourteen lines

**iambic pentameter** rhythmic pattern that alternates between unstressed and stressed syllables

**doff** shed, give up

**counsel** private thoughts

*As you read the passage below* try to pay attention to the rhythm of each line.

Juliet: [*not knowing Romeo hears her*] O Romeo,
　　　Romeo, wherefore art thou Romeo?
　　　Deny thy father and refuse thy name,
　　　Or if thou wilt not, be but sworn my love,
　　　And I'll no longer be a Capulet.
Romeo: [*aside*] Shall I hear more, or shall I speak at this?
Juliet: 'Tis but thy name that is my enemy.
　　　Thou art thyself, though not a Montague.
　　　What's Montague? It is nor hand, nor foot,
　　　Nor arm, nor face, nor any other part
　　　Belonging to a man. O, be some other name!
　　　What's in a name? That which we call a rose
　　　By any other word would smell as sweet.
　　　So Romeo would, were he not Romeo called,
　　　Retain that dear perfection which he owes
　　　Without that title. Romeo, **doff** thy name,
　　　And for thy name—which is no part of thee—
　　　Take all myself.

> What is Romeo's last name? What is Juliet's?
> _____
> _____

> What does Juliet's reference to a rose mean?
> _____
> _____

Romeo:  [*to Juliet*] I take thee at thy word.
  Call me but love and I'll be new baptized.
  Henceforth I never will be Romeo.
Juliet: What man art thou that, thus bescreened in
  night,
  So stumblest on my **counsel**?
Romeo:  By a name
  I know not how to tell thee who I am.
  My name, dear saint, is hateful to myself
  Because it is an enemy to thee.
  Had I it written, I would tear the word.
Juliet: My ears have yet not drunk a hundred words
  Of thy tongue's uttering, yet I know the sound.
  Art thou not Romeo, and a Montague?
Romeo:  Neither, fair maid, if either thee dislike.
Juliet: How cam'st thou hither, tell me, and
  wherefore?
  The orchard walls are high and hard to climb,
  And the place death, considering who thou art,
  If any of my kinsmen find thee here.

> What does Romeo mean by the use of the word *baptized*?
> _____
> _____

## ANALYZING LITERATURE

**1. Main Idea** What is the problem that Romeo and Juliet are discussing?

_____

_____

**2. Critical Thinking: Drawing Inferences** How do you think Romeo and Juliet will proceed with their relationship? Why?

_____

_____

## ACTIVITY

Conduct research on both iambic pentameter and sonnets in order to fully understand each term. Now write your own sonnet in iambic pentameter about some aspect of Northern Europe.

# "The Scream" by Edvard Munch

**ABOUT THE ARTIST** Edvard Munch was born in Oslo, Norway, in 1863. His work, an **antecedent** of the **expressionist** movement, often depicted shocking themes of fear and death. "The Scream" is one of his most famous works.

**VOCABULARY**

**antecedent** something that comes before

**expressionist** representing feelings and moods rather than reality

**temperament** the way a person thinks, behaves, and reacts

*As you examine the painting,* consider the feelings and emotions the artist is trying to convey. Notice how the painting makes you feel.

Munch identified his paintings as "symbolism: nature viewed through *temperament.*"

In 2004, the original painting was stolen from the Munch Museum in Oslo. It has not yet been recovered.

Source: Edvard Much, The Scream, 1910. Photo credit: Erich Lessing/Art Resource, NY

## WHAT DID YOU LEARN?

1. What physical feature common to the Norwegian coast is depicted in the painting?

   _____

   _____

2. Use at least three adjectives to describe how the person is feeling in the painting and give reasons for your answer.

   _____

   _____

3. How would you describe the person's appearance?

   _____

   _____

4. How is nature depicted in this painting?

   _____

   _____

# Understanding Northern Europe

The geography of Northern Europe makes it a place of extreme physical diversity. You can find rolling hills, high cliffs, volcanoes, and shooting geysers. You might see lush valleys, rocky terrain, or areas where the climate is so cold that only grass and moss can grow.

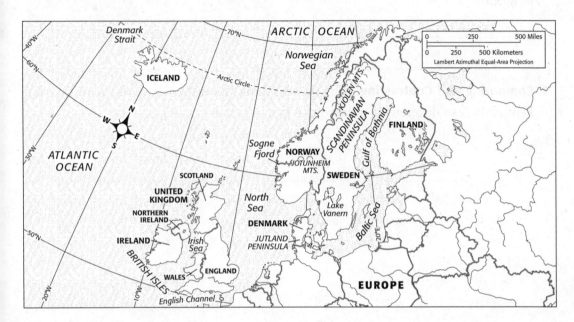

## MAP ACTIVITY

**1.** Color the countries of the United Kingdom with a yellow pencil.

**2.** Use a green pencil to shade the countries of Scandinavia.

**3.** Use a red pencil to outline at least three fjords.

**4.** Place an "X" in all areas on the map that were once conquered or settled by the Vikings.

## ANALYZING MAPS

**1. Movement** About how many miles would the Vikings have sailed to get from Sogne Fjord to the Gulf of Bothnia?

_____

_____

**2. Location** How do you think the location of Northern Ireland contributes to the conflict there?

_____

_____

**3. Location** Describe the location of Northern Europe in terms of latitude and longitude.

_____

_____

**4. Comparing and Contrasting** Why do you think the east coast of the Scandinavian Peninsula is so different in appearance from the west coast?

_____

_____

**Northern Europe**

## Social Studies Skills

# Writing to Learn

## LEARN THE SKILL

Writing is an active process that can help you learn new information.
The act of writing helps focus your attention. It can also encourage
you to think analytically about a particular topic. Putting something in
your own words helps you discover what you do and do not understand
about a subject.

Some students may prefer to jot down quick notes or make outlines.
Others may learn better by writing more extensively, in paragraph-style.
Usually, writing to learn involves informal writing, such as note-taking,
journal writing, letters, free-writing, or personal responses.

## PRACTICE THE SKILL

Read back over your notes from this chapter. Then set a timer for
15 minutes. On a separate piece of paper, write down all the details you
remember from the chapter. Try to write continuously for the full 15
minutes, even if you have to repeat something you already wrote.

If you had trouble writing for the full time, look at your notes from
the chapter once more. Are they so brief that they did not make sense
to you when you reviewed them? Or are they so long that all your focus
was on writing rather than on understanding the information?

## Northern Europe

# The Vikings Abroad

*Vikings* is the term we use today for the people who, from the AD 700s to the 1000s, left their homelands in Scandinavia for other lands. They began three centuries of raiding, trading, exploring, and colonizing. The Viking movements are a good example of migration.

## REASONS FOR MIGRATION

Many people have wondered what prompted the Viking expansion. People migrate, or permanently relocate, in response to push and pull factors. Push factors are things about a person's current location that are undesirable. These factors may "push" the person to leave. Pull factors are the things about a new location that are attractive and "pull" a person toward it. Not enough land for farming, herding, or hunting was an important push factor for the Vikings. Also, some Vikings wanted to escape the rule of a particular king or chief.

Many historians now think that the increasing wealth of Europe was the biggest pull factor. By the 700s, trade was picking up again after having collapsed with the fall of the Roman Empire. Treasure was piling up in churches, monasteries, and other religious centers. Increased opportunities to plunder attracted the Vikings.

## BARRIERS TO MIGRATION

For any group or individual, there are also barriers to migration. These can be physical, cultural, economic, or legal. The major barrier to migration for the Vikings was that the native peoples did not want them in their lands. In some places, the Vikings were defeated militarily. In other places, they raided successfully. They gained treasure and slaves, but no land. In yet other places, the Vikings were able to establish towns and villages and bring in hundreds or thousands of settlers. Some people paid the Vikings to go away. These bribes were called Danegelds. Others offered the Vikings land to settle on; this is what happened in Normandy. Yet other groups invited the Vikings to become their rulers. These groups included the Slavic people in the area of present-day Novgorod (see map). In this way, the Vikings, who were sometimes called the Rus, became the founders of Russia. It is clear from the Viking example that immigrants may receive a variety of responses from others when they arrive.

## EFFECTS OF MIGRATION

Migration can have many consequences. For example, the Vikings who settled in the lands where they were raiders or traders mixed into the local society. They learned the local language, married local people, and adopted new religions such as Christianity.

The Viking expansion had many effects on people's lives. Sometimes trade was disrupted, but at other times it was improved. Boat design improved with Viking technology. Numerous place-names in eastern England developed from Viking words. Words such as *window*, *husband*, *sky*, *anger*, *low*, *ugly*, *wrong*, *happy*, *thrive*, *ill*, *die*, *bread*, and *eggs* came into English this way.

The Vikings brought democratic ideas with them to Iceland. There they established the Althing, the world's first parliament. Upon arrival, they also immediately set to work transforming the landscape of the island, heavily exploiting the walrus (which apparently died out rather quickly) and the great auk (which eventually became extinct in the 1800s). Wood-cutting and the introduction of domesticated animals and plants led to the destruction of much of the natural vegetation of the island.

The effects of the Viking emigration on their homelands were several. Wealth from raiding and trading poured into the region. Some wealth was undoubtedly carried back to Scandinavia by returning migrants. Some Vikings went back to their old homes, rather than staying in the new land. For every migration stream, there is a return migration stream. People who returned were either disappointed with the new place or they had always intended to go home.

## YOU ARE THE GEOGRAPHER

Use the map on the next page and an atlas to answer the following questions.

**1.** What three modern countries were the Viking homelands?

_____

**2.** From which islands did Vikings go west to Iceland and beyond?

_____

**3.** From which countries did Vikings go south to western and southern Europe?

_____

**4.** From which country did Vikings go east to eastern Europe, Russia, and Asia?

_____

**5.** What is the latest date on the map for an area "occupied or dominated" by Vikings? Where is it? This place is part of what country today?

_____

_____

Write an essay that compares and contrasts a later example of migration to the Viking example. This could be the migration story of an individual or family with whom you are familiar or of a large group such as Scandinavians coming to the United States after the Civil War or Mexicans drawn to California or Texas in the 1900s. Discuss push and pull factors, barriers to migration, and the consequences of the migration. Explain how your example of migration is similar to and different from the experience of the Vikings.

# The Viking Migration

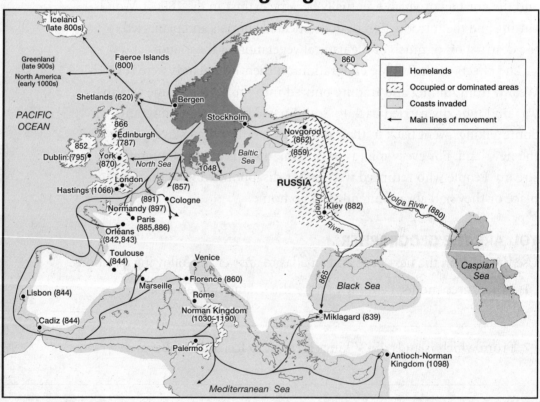

# Connecting Europe by Chunnel

*In May 1994 Great Britain's Queen Elizabeth and French president François Mitterrand opened the tunnel that connects their two nations under the English Channel. The Channel Tunnel, or "Chunnel" as it is popularly known, is the result of 200 years of hopes and plans to link Great Britain and France. To learn about the Chunnel, study the passage, map, and diagram and answer the questions.*

The 31-mile-long Chunnel is really three parallel tunnels: two for trains and a service tunnel. It snakes from Folkestone, England, to Coquelles, France, an average of 150 feet below the seabed. Drive onto a train at one end; stay in your car and drive off . . . at the other [end] 35 minutes later. . . Passenger trains . . . provide through service: London to Paris in three hours; London to Brussels in three hours, ten minutes. The Chunnel rewrites geography, at least in the English psyche [mind]. The moat has been breached. Britain is no longer an island.

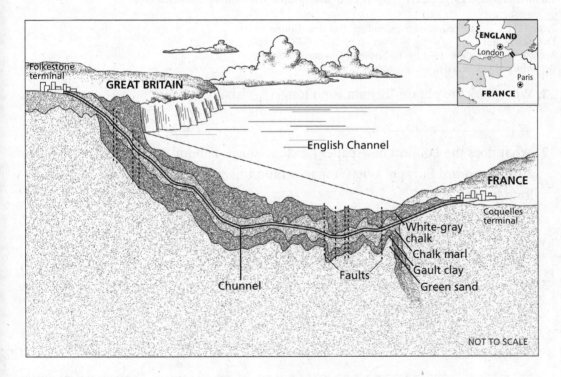

On a clear day . . . on the north coast of France, you can look across the Channel and see the faint shimmer of chalk cliffs on the English coast. It is 22 miles to Dover as the bluebird flies. Ninety minutes by ferry, 40 minutes by hovercraft. . . Odds of a gale on any day in winter are one in seven. Now neither freight nor passengers need be held hostage by a heaving sea.

. . . Dreams of a cross-Channel connection have materialized, only to evaporate, 26 times before. Albert Matheiu, a French engineer, proposed the first plan in 1802. . . Napoleon, Britain's archenemy, approved, and there's the curse. . . Why, after two centuries, did the two ancient foes finally take the plunge? A congruence [alignment] of stars and planets[?] . . . Sir Alastair Morton, the British chairman of Eurotunnel—the Anglo-French company that owns and operates the tunnel [says it is] "more likely a congruence of political tides and currents" . . . On his wall is a copy of the legendary London newspaper headline: "Fog in Channel. Continent Cut Off" . . .

Other converging currents: a tidal wave of 220 banks from 26 nations to finance the project. British and French industries desperate for work (the tunnel [construction] employed as many as 15,000 workers).

"The tunnel's come about because Britain finally feels secure," adds Sir Christopher Mallaby, Britain's ambassador to France. Still, the country just can't go it alone. Britain, which snubbed the rest of Europe for years, has joined the European Union . . . The island mentality has eased. . .

From "The Light at the End of the Chunnel" (retitled "Connecting Europe by Chunnel") by Cathy Newman from *National Geographic*, May 1994. Copyright © 1994 by the **National Geographic Society.** Reproduced by permission of the publisher.

**1.** What does the phrase "Britain is no longer an island" mean?

_____

**2.** What does the London newspaper headline suggest about Britons' traditional attitude toward Europe? What impact would this view likely have had on plans for a tunnel?

_____

_____

**3.** Why would the engineers have chosen to construct the tunnel in the marl layer rather than choosing a depth that was higher or lower?

_____

_____

**4.** What geological dangers to the Chunnel are shown by the drawing? What risks do they present for the future of Chunnel operations?

_____

_____

# Using Context Clues—Synonyms

As you read, you may occasionally encounter a word or phrase that you do not know. When that happens, use the words and sentences around the unfamiliar word—context clues—to help you determine the word's meaning. Sometimes the clues you find will be words or phrases that have the same meaning as the unfamiliar word. These are synonyms.

## PRACTICING USING CONTEXT CLUES

Use context clues to determine the meaning of the underlined word in the following excerpts from your chapter. Write the meaning of the underlined word in the space provided.

**1.** As the glaciers flowed slowly downhill, they carved long, winding channels, or <u>fjords</u>, into Norway's coastline.

_____

**2.** Iceland also has an unusual resource, <u>geothermal energy</u>, energy produced from the heat of Earth's interior.

_____

**3.** Early settlers built <u>Stonehenge</u>, an ancient monument, some 5,000 years ago.

_____

**4.** One similarity is their common <u>ancestry</u>. Many people in the British Isles trace their heritage to the early invaders of the region, such as the Celts, Angles, and Saxons.

_____

**5.** <u>Oslo</u>, the capital of Norway, is the country's leading seaport, as well as its industrial and cultural center.

_____

_____

**6.** Because some 80 percent of the island is covered in a thick ice sheet, much land on the island is <u>uninhabitable</u>, or not able to support human settlement.

_____

Using Context Clues—Synonyms, *continued*                    Focus on Reading

## CREATING YOUR OWN CONTEXT CLUES

| | | |
|---|---|---|
| colonies | fertile | marine |
| popular culture | populous | primary resources |
| prosperous | Vikings | |

The word bank contains words and terms from your chapter. Choose
five words and use each of them in a sentence about Northern Europe
that includes a context clue.

1. _____

_____

_____

2. _____

_____

_____

3. _____

_____

_____

4. _____

_____

_____

5. _____

_____

_____

**Northern Europe**

# Focus on Writing

## Writing a Letter

Letters are a great way to stay in touch with family and friends. Gather
information about Northern Europe as you read the chapter. Now,
imagine you are traveling through this region. Write a letter to your
friends and family at home in which you describe what you have seen
and learned in your travels.

### PREWRITING

**1. Describing the Physical Geography** Take notes on the physical features,
resources, and climates of Northern Europe. Include information about the
following: fjords, coastlines, terrain, countries of the British Isles, countries of
Scandinavia, geothermal energy, primary resources, and the North Atlantic Drift.

**2. Writing about the British Isles** What information about the British Isles could
you include in a letter to someone who has never visited the area? Consider the
following: early history, the British Empire, the Industrial Revolution, Ireland's
famine, popular culture and traditions, disputes, and current economic and
political situations.

**3. Writing about Scandinavia** Add information about Scandinavia to your notes.
Include details about the following: early history, the Vikings, cultural and
economic traits of each country, natural resources, and geysers.

### WRITING

**4. Preparing to Write your Letter** Decide how to organize it. You may imagine that
you are writing a bit at the end of each day of travel. Or you may imagine that
you are coming home on the plane and writing a summary of the trip.

**5. Writing the Letter** Try to let it read like a real letter rather than a report on
Northern Europe. Include your imagined reaction to what you have seen and
done in Northern Europe. What were your favorite things about your imaginary
trip? Was there anything you did not enjoy?

## EVALUATING AND PROOFREADING

**6. Evaluating your Letter** Would someone reading your letter get a good sense of the geography, history, and personality of Northern Europe, even if he or she knew nothing about the region?

**Rubric** Use this rubric to check that you have included all the required information in your letter.

- Have you included information about the physical geography and climate of Northern Europe?

- Have you included details about the history, people, culture, and current issues of the British Isles?

- Have you included details about the history, people, culture, and current issues of Scandinavia?

- Have you included your personal reaction to the people and places you've seen?

**7. Proofreading your Letter** Last, check the following:

- Capitalization and spelling of all proper names and places

- Punctuation, grammar, and spelling

## Northern Europe

# Chapter Review

**BIG IDEAS**

1. Northern Europe is a region of unique physical features, rich resources, and diverse climates.

2. Close cultural and historical ties link the people of the British Isles today.

3. Scandinavia has developed into one of the most stable and prosperous regions in Europe.

## REVIEWING VOCABULARY, TERMS, AND PLACES

Use the clues provided to fill in the crossword puzzle below.

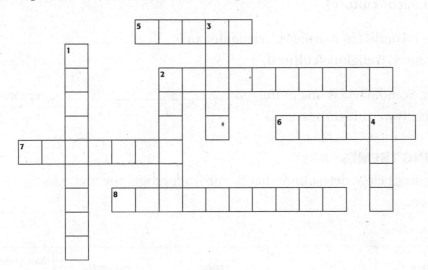

**Across**

2. Hot springs and geysers in Iceland produce _____ energy.

5. Much of Northern Europe has a mild climate due to the North Atlantic _____.

6. the capital of the United Kingdom

7. Scandinavian warriors who sailed longboats

8. Britain's legislative body

**Down**

1. capital of a Scandinavian country known for being neutral for the past 200 years

2. a spring that shoots hot water and steam into the air

3. deep inlet of the sea carved by melting glaciers

4. leading seaport and industrial center, as well as Norway's capital

## COMPREHENSION AND CRITICAL THINKING

Read each sentence and fill in the blank with the word in the word pair
that best completes the sentence.

**1.** Natural resources found in Northern Europe include _____.
   (**timber and fish/glaciers and cliffs**)

**2.** Iceland and Greenland are often considered part of _____.
   (**Scandinavia/the British Isles**)

**3.** British _____ has influenced much of the world.
   (**Parliament/culture**)

**4.** There is conflict in Northern Ireland due to _____
   differences. (**religious/cultural**)

**5.** Today, Scandinavia is one of the most _____ regions in
   Europe. (**war-ridden/peaceful**)

## REVIEWING THEMES

Using the lists below, determine what theme from geography they have
in common.

**Themes**

| location | place | region | movement | human-environment interaction |
|----------|-------|--------|----------|-------------------------------|
|          |       |        |          |                               |

_____ **1.** longboats, timber, hydroelectric energy

_____ **2.** fjords, long coastline, major seaports

_____ **3.** marine west coast, North Atlantic Drift,
                          wealthy and powerful

## REVIEW ACTIVITY: TRAVEL BROCHURE

Create a marketing brochure for a cruise that travels throughout
Northern Europe. Using the political map at the beginning of your
textbook chapter, describe the route and stops your cruise ship would
make. Include photos from newspapers, magazines, or other sources
your teacher approves. Make sure you include information about
climate, physical features, economics, history, and culture.

**Eastern Europe**                         Vocabulary Builder

| | | | |
|---|---|---|---|
| Adriatic Sea | Balkan Mountains | Balkan Peninsula | Carpathians |
| Chernobyl | Danube | function | radiation |

**DIRECTIONS** On the line provided before each statement, write **T** if a statement is true and **F** if a statement is false. If the statement is false, write the correct term on the line after each sentence that makes the sentence a true statement.

_____ 1. The <u>Balkan Mountains</u> are a low mountain range that stretch in a long arc from the Alps to the Black Sea area.

_____

_____ 2. The Black Sea serves the same function as the <u>Carpathians</u>; they are both important trade routes.

_____

_____ 3. A nuclear explosion at the <u>Chernobyl</u> power plant released huge amounts of radiation into the air.

_____

_____ 4. The <u>Danube</u> begins in Germany and flows through nine countries before emptying into the Black Sea.

_____

_____ 5. One of the largest in Europe, the <u>Adriatic Sea</u> extends south into the Mediterranean Sea.

_____

| Baltic Republics | embroidery | infrastructure |
| Krakow | Poland | Warsaw |

**DIRECTIONS** Read each sentence and fill in the blank with the word in the word pair that best completes the sentence.

**1.** The Soviets failed to build a strong _____, which has weakened the economies of the Baltic states. (**embroidery/infrastructure**)

**2.** By the Middle Ages, the kingdoms of Lithuania and _____ were large and strong. (**Poland/Warsaw**)

**3.** _____ is the capital of Poland. (**Warsaw/Krakow**)

**4.** The _____ include(s) Latvia, Estonia, and Lithuania. (**infrastructure/Baltic Republics**)

**5.** _____ is a type of decorative sewing that is popular among people in the Baltic region. (**Krakow/Embroidery**)

**DIRECTIONS** Choose four of the terms from the word bank. On a separate sheet of paper, use these words to write a short story that relates to the section.

Europe and Russia

# Eastern Europe

# Vocabulary Builder

## Section 3

| | | |
|---|---|---|
| Budapest | Kiev | Magyars |
| Prague | Slavs | |
| Commonwealth of Independent States | | |

**DIRECTIONS** Read each sentence and choose the correct term from the word bank to replace the underlined phrases. Write the term in the space provided and then define the term in your own words.

**1.** Members of <u>this alliance</u> meet in Minsk to discuss issues such as trade and

immigration. (**Commonwealth of Independent States/Magyars**) _____

_____

Your definition: _____

_____

**2.** This <u>group of fierce invaders</u> swept into Hungary and established a strong culture

there. (**Magyars/Slavs**) _____

Your definition: _____

_____

**3.** <u>This</u> is the capital city of the Czech Republic. (**Budapest/Prague**) _____

Your definition: _____

_____

**4.** The Rus established <u>this city</u> in the 800s, which still stands in Ukraine today.

(**Prague/Kiev**) _____

Your definition: _____

_____

**5.** Ukraine, Belarus, and Moldavia were settled by <u>this group of people</u>.

(**Magyars/Slavs**) _____

Your definition: _____

_____

Europe and Russia

# Eastern Europe

# Vocabulary Builder

## Section 4

| | | |
|---|---|---|
| Balkans | ethnic cleansing | implications |
| Mostar | Orthodox | Roma |
| Slavic | Soviet Union | Yugoslavia |

**DIRECTIONS** Look at each set of terms following each number. On the line provided, write the letter of the term that does not relate to the others.

_____ **1. a.** Protestant    **b.** Orthodox   **c.** Catholic   **d.** Slavic

_____ **2. a.** World War I    **b.** Serbia   **c.** Germanic   **d.** Austro-Hungarians

_____ **3. a.** Albania    **b.** Hungary   **c.** Croatia   **d.** Slovenia

_____ **4. a.** Macedonia    **b.** Yugoslavia   **c.** violence   **d.** ethnic cleansing

_____ **5. a.** Roma    **b.** Greeks   **c.** Romans   **d.** Ottomans

**DIRECTIONS** Choose at least three of the terms from the word bank. On a separate sheet of paper, use these words to write a summary of what you learned in Section 4.

Europe and Russia

# Estée Lauder
## 1908–2004

**HOW SHE AFFECTED THE WORLD** Estée Lauder was named one of the 20 most influential business leaders of the century by *Time* Magazine in 1998. She was the only woman on the list. With a natural talent for marketing and an eye for beauty, Lauder turned her home-based skin cream product into a multi-billion dollar cosmetics empire.

Bettmann/CORBIS

*As you read the biography below, think about how Lauder's shrewd business sense and* **innovation** *led to her success.*

### VOCABULARY
**innovation** introduction of new methods
**promotional** free samples of a new product in order to sell it
**fragrance** perfume

Estée Lauder was born Josephine Esther Mentzer, the daughter of working-class Hungarian Jewish immigrants in Queens, New York. As a child, her family often called her Esty, short for Esther, which became Estée later in her career.

During the 1930s, Lauder's uncle, a chemist, began making face creams as an experiment in his laboratory. Lauder became interested in the experiment and soon began making her own batches of face cream in her kitchen.

Even though Lauder had a talent for making face creams, her true gift was selling the product. Lauder began visiting beauty salons where she gave free demonstrations to women. The women soon became paying customers.

After several years of perfecting her product and sales techniques, Lauder negotiated a large order with a major department store, Saks Fifth Avenue, in New York City. Lauder and her husband made the face creams and packaged the product. Saks sold out of the face cream in two days.

Estée Lauder, both the company and the businesswoman, achieved continued success after the sale at Saks. Lauder began traveling to different department stores around the country, persuading them to promote and sell her product. She began using what are now two very successful sales tools—free samples and **promotional** gifts with the purchase of a product.

In 1953, Estée Lauder's name became even more popular with the introduction of a new bath oil and **fragrance** called Youth Dew. Over the next several decades, Lauder, with the help of her two sons, expanded the company into a multi-billion dollar corporation. Lauder's skin care products, cosmetics, and fragrances are now available in more than 100 countries around the globe.

Estée Lauder retired from the company in 1994, and she died ten years later. However, with the continued success of the cosmetics empire that still bears her name, Estée Lauder will not soon be forgotten.

## WHAT DID YOU LEARN?

**1. Recall**  How did Estée Lauder promote her products? Give at least three examples.

_____

_____

**2. Evaluate**  What qualities did Estée Lauder possess to help her become a successful businessperson? Explain which quality you think is most important.

_____

_____

_____

## ACTIVITY

Use the Internet, magazines, and newspapers to find information about other successful businesspeople—past and present. Create a list of three businesspeople and state the major accomplishments of each.

**Eastern Europe**                                        Biography

# MADELEINE ALBRIGHT

### 1937–

**HOW SHE AFFECTED THE WORLD** In 1997, Madeleine Albright became the first female U.S. Secretary of State. This position also made her the highest-ranking female in the history of the United States government.

*As you read the biography below,* think about how many important political positions Albright held throughout her career.

Wally McNamee/CORBIS

Madeleine Albright was born in Prague, Czechoslovakia. Her family fled the country twice—first to escape the Nazis and later to escape the Communists. They moved to the United States in 1946. Madeleine became a United States citizen while attending college in 1957.

Albright's studies focused on international relations. After receiving her first college degree, she went on to study international relations at Johns Hopkins University and later earned a doctorate degree from Columbia University. Albright also became a student of languages. In addition to Czech and English, Madeleine became fluent in French, Russian, and Polish.

After completing her studies, Albright worked in various U.S. government positions. In the late 1970s and early 1980s, Albright worked as a staff member on the National Security Council. She handled foreign policy **legislation** while working for the White House.

The 1980s were a busy time for Albright. In 1981, she co-founded a nonprofit research organization called the Center for National Policy. In 1982 Albright became a professor at

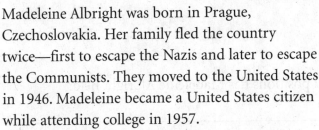

**VOCABULARY**

**legislation** law

**fellowship** money to support a student or scholar

**feat** accomplishment

**reclusive** secluded

Georgetown University in Washington, D.C. She

was also awarded a **fellowship** at the Woodrow
Wilson International Center for Scholars at the
Smithsonian Institution between 1981 and 1982.

Ten years later, Albright became the United States
Ambassador to the United Nations. She also served
as a member of President Clinton's cabinet.

In 1997 Madeleine Albright became the first
woman to hold the position of United States
Secretary of State. In 2000 Albright accomplished
another major **feat** in her position as Secretary
of State when she met with the **reclusive** North
Korean leader, Kim Jong Il.

Since her retirement, Albright has started her
own business, teaches, and has written a book
about her life's accomplishments entitled *Madam
Secretary.*

## WHAT DID YOU LEARN?

**1. Recall** What important political positions has Madeleine Albright held?

_____

_____

**2. Draw a Conclusion** How did Albright's Czech heritage help her to be successful
in politics?

_____

_____

## ACTIVITY

Suppose you were asked to say a few words at Madeleine Albright's
retirement party. Make a brief outline of what you will say, then present
your speech to the rest of the class.

# The Bridge on the Drina
## by Ivo Andric

**ABOUT THE READING** Ivo Andric won a Nobel Prize for Literature in 1961 for *The Bridge on the Drina*. The novel offers a historic overview of the relationship between Serbs and Muslims in the former Yugoslavia during the rule of the Ottoman Empire. The excerpt below describes the importance of the bridge to the people who live near it.

**VOCABULARY**

**cultivated**  prepared for planting crops

**indispensable**  absolutely necessary or required

**inevitably**  cannot be avoided

**imperishable**  something that will not die or decay

*As you read the passage below,* look for signs that the author held great respect for the bridge.

Here, where the Drina flows with the whole force of its green and foaming waters from the apparently closed mass of the dark steep mountains, stands a great clean-cut stone bridge with eleven wide sweeping arches . . . Looked at from a distance through the broad arches of the white bridge it seems as if one can see not only the green Drina, but all that fertile and **cultivated** countryside and the southern sky above.

> Underline words that describe the appearance of the bridge.

. . . [T]he bridge, uniting the two parts of the Sarajevo road, linked the town with its surrounding villages.

Actually, to say "linked" was just as true as to say that the sun rises in the morning so that men may see around them and finish their daily tasks, and sets in the evening that they may be able to sleep and rest from the labors of the day. For this great stone bridge, a rare structure of unique beauty, such as many richer and busier towns do not possess (There are only two others such as this in

> The author compares the bridge with the rising and setting sun. This powerful comparison shows that the people relied heavily on the bridge, just as they relied on the sun to rise and set each day.

*The Bridge on the Drina*, from *The Ivo Andric Foundation* web site, accessed at http:www.ivoandric.org/yu/html/body_andric_s_treasury. html, September 23, 2005. Copyright © by Ivo Andric. Reproduced by permission of **The Ivo Andric Foundation.**

the whole Empire, they used to say in old times)
was the one real and permanent crossing in the
whole middle und upper course of the Drina and
an **indispensable** link on the road between Bosnia
and Serbia . . . The town and its outskirts were only
the settlements, which always and **inevitably** grow
up around an important center of communications
and on either side of great and important bridges.

> Sarajevo is one of the cities that served as an important center of communications, helped by the bridge over the Drina.

   Here also in time the houses crowded together
and the settlements multiplied at both ends of the
bridge. The town owed its existence to the bridge
and grew out of it as if from an **imperishable** root.

## ANALYZING LITERATURE

**1. Main Idea** According to the passage, what functions did the bridge serve?

_____

_____

**2. Critical Thinking: Make an Inference** What would happen to the towns if the
bridge on the Drina no longer existed?

_____

_____

## ACTIVITY

Imagine that you are a social scientist conducting research on the
importance of bridges in a community. Identify two significant bridges
in the United States and explain how each bridge is important to the
communities they connect.

# The 1956 Hungarian Revolution

**ABOUT THE READING** In 1 56, Russia invaded Hungary to stop the Hungarians from revolting against Communist rule. *he un arian e o ution istor in Docu ents* reports some of the Hungarian actions that took place in Hungary on November , 1 56—during the Cold War.

**VOCABULARY**

**sabotage** to destroy secretly and on purpose

**infiltrate** sneak into

**undermine** go behind the authority's back

**detain** hold for questioning

*As you read the ex erpt below, try to determine from which perspective the report is written— Russian or Hungarian.*

Having lost the opportunity to fight by means of armed uprising, <u>the reactionary forces</u> use new methods to pursue their counterrevolutionary goals—primarily, strikes and **sabotage**.

> The reactionary forces are Hungarian citizens who rose up against the Soviet troops that invaded their country.

Last week, the reaction attempted to involve a large segment of workers and service personnel in a general strike in the main branches of industry and on the railroad.

<u>Exploiting the situation</u>, where the party organizations at the enterprises were destroyed during the days of reaction and were being rebuilt very slowly, the reactionary elements began to **infiltrate** the plants and the mines. They try to **undermine** the work in various ways by <u>inspiring the workers to go on strike until the government satisfies their demands</u> . . .

> *pl it* means to take advantage of a situation when it is already weak.

> The demands of the Hungarian rebels were to have the Soviet troops leave Hungary, to have their Hungarian leader put back in office, and to allow more than one political party in the Hungarian government.

From "Document No. 9: Situation Report from Malenkov-Suslov-Aristov, November 22, 1956" from *The 19 Hungarian Revolution A History of Documents, A National Security Archive Electronic Briefing Book,* edited by Malcolm Byrne, accessed at http:www.gwu.edu/~nsarchiv/NSAEBB/NSAEBB76/, on October 10, 2005. Published by The National Security Archive, Washington, D.C., 2002.

. . . In order to find and eliminate underground rebel centers, our security officials, together with the Hungarian police, worked on arresting and **detaining** persons who participated most actively in the armed riots. <u>Altogether, 1,473 people were arrested in addition to 5,820 persons who were detained and remain under investigation</u>. Leaders and organizers of the riots, persons who supplied the rebels with weapons and ammunition, and also members of the so-called revolutionary committees active during the riots are subject to arrest.

. . . So far, we have not been able to arrest the military leader of the rebellion . . . Our comrades, together with Hungarian comrades, are engaged in the search for those people.

> What does the large number of people arrested and detained tell you about the Hungarian revolution?
>
> _____
> _____
> _____

## WHAT DID YOU LEARN?

**1.** What attitude does the author of this report express toward the Hungarian revolutionaries? Give an example from the passage to support your answer.

_____

_____

**2.** Do you think the demands of the Hungarian revolutionaries were fair? Explain your answer.

_____

_____

**3.** After reading the excerpt, which side do you support—the Hungarians or the Soviets? Why?

_____

_____

# Soviet Domination of Eastern Europe

The Soviet Union occupied the Eastern European territories after World War II. By the late 1940s, Communist leaders were put in control of the occupied states of Eastern Europe. Soviet troops would use force if the Eastern European states tried to revolt against Communist rule. But the Eastern European states maintained hope that one day they would be independent again. After four decades, the Berlin Wall—a symbol of Communist dictatorship in Eastern Europe—was torn down on November 9, 1989. The transition from communism to democracy had begun for most of Eastern Europe.

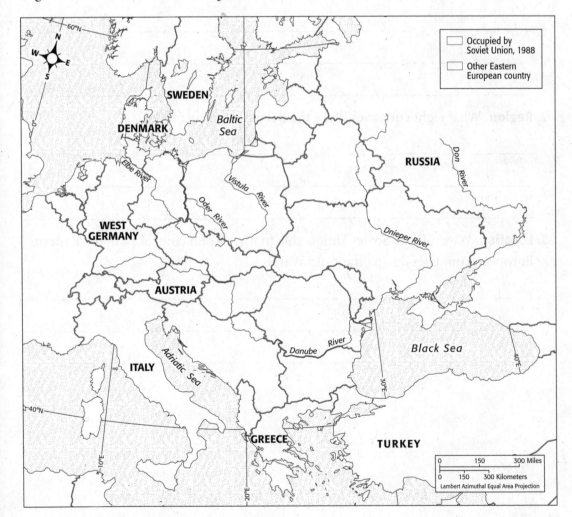

## MAP ACTIVITY

**1.** Label the following Eastern European countries on the map: Estonia, Latvia, Lithuania, Belorussia, Ukraine, Moldova, Romania, Bulgaria, Albania, Yugoslavia, Hungary, Czechoslovakia, East Germany, and Poland.

**2.** Use a yellow pencil or marker to shade the Eastern European countries that were occupied by the Soviet Union in 1988.

**3.** Use a light blue pencil or marker to highlight the remaining Eastern European countries.

**4.** Create a map legend reflecting the colors you added to the map.

## ANALYZING MAPS

**1. Place**  Which Eastern European country split into five different republics after the Cold War? What are the names of the republics?

_____

_____

_____

**2. Region**  What eight countries share the Balkan Peninsula today?

_____

_____

_____

**3. Location**  Why was the Soviet Union able to invade and control so many Eastern European countries during the Cold War?

_____

_____

_____

**Eastern Europe**

Social Studies Skills

## Critical Thinking

# Analyzing Benefits and Costs

### LEARN THE SKILL

Before you make a decision or take a side in a discussion, it helps to
make a list of all the pros and cons (benefits or costs). After making
such a list, you may decide that your idea is indeed a good one—or
that you need to change it. Creating a chart can make it easier to analyze both sides of the decision. Remember, not all benefits and costs are
related to money. Sometimes a benefit could be a new opportunity, and
a cost could mean you have to give something up.

### PRACTICE THE SKILL

Reread the Case Study feature in Section 4 of your textbook chapter.
As you read, use the chart below to take notes about the breakup of
Yugoslavia. Record possible benefits and costs to the region's economy
that would result from the breakup of Yugoslavia.

| BENEFITS | COSTS |
|----------|-------|
|          |       |
|          |       |
|          |       |
|          |       |
|          |       |
|          |       |

### APPLY THE SKILL

You are thinking of starting a business in Budapest, Hungary, that
shuttles people across the Danube River from Buda to Pest and back. List
the possible benefits and costs of this business idea on a chart like the one
above. Use the information on your chart to help you make your decision.

**Eastern Europe**                    Geography for Life

# Cities and Rivers in Eastern Europe

A city needs a good site and a good situation to grow in size and power.
Good sites often have flat, well-drained land, available water, and (in
the past) defensibility from attack. In almost all cases, a good situation
has meant being linked to other places, including resource regions and
other cities. Before the advent of the railroad or the automobile, waterways provided some of the most important links between places. Both
Eastern and Western Europe illustrate that a location on a major river
or one of its tributaries is favorable to city growth.

## YOU ARE THE GEOGRAPHER

**1.** You will need to use the map on the third page to complete this activity. Begin by
using an atlas to correctly identify and label the following Eastern European
countries: *Poland, the Czech Republic, Slovakia, Hungary, Slovenia, Croatia,*
*Bosnia and Herzegovina, Yugoslavia, Albania, Macedonia, Bulgaria,* and *Romania.*
Also label *Germany* and *Austria,* although they are not Eastern European. Try to
label the country names in such a way that you will have room to write the river
names along the rivers and the city names near the dots provided.

**2.** The five longest rivers in Eastern Europe (excluding Belarus, Ukraine, and Russia)
are the *Danube,* the *Elbe,* the *Vistula,* the *Tisza,* and the *Sava.* Not all of these
rivers are entirely within Eastern Europe. The Danube actually begins in Germany,
and the Elbe ends there. Use an atlas to correctly identify and label these five
rivers on the map. Notice that the Sava and the Tisza are major tributaries of the
Danube. Also identify and label these additional tributaries of the Danube: the
*Bosna,* the *Iskur,* and the *Dambovita,* plus two tributaries of the Elbe: the *Havel*
and the *Vltava.* Highlight all of these waterways with a blue felt pen.

**3.** Use the atlas to identify and label the Eastern European capital cities: *Warsaw,*
*Prague, Bratislava, Budapest, Ljubljana, Zagreb, Sarajevo, Belgrade, Tirane, Skopje,*
*Sofia,* and *Bucharest.* Also label *Berlin* and *Vienna* in Western Europe.

**4.** Which national capitals are located on the Danube River system?

_____

**5.** Which national capitals are located on the Elbe River system?

_____

**6.** Which national capital is located on the Vistula?

_____

**7.** Which capitals are not on any of the five rivers named above? Are they on other rivers (check your atlas)?

_____

**8.** What is the main direction of flow of the Elbe? Into what body of water does it empty? What do you suppose happened to the amount of barge traffic on the Elbe when the "Iron Curtain" came down after World War II, leaving Hamburg on one side and many upstream cities on the other?

_____

_____

_____

**9.** What is the main direction of flow of the Danube? Into what body of water does it empty? Now look in your atlas for the Rhine River in Western Europe. Also find the Main River, one of its tributaries. Label these on your map and highlight them in green. The Rhine is a major river like the Danube that flows through many countries and cities. Can you think of reasons why the amount of traffic on the Rhine is much greater than that on the Danube, despite the Danube's much greater length?

_____

_____

_____

**10.** In 1998 the Danube and Rhine River systems were linked when the Rhine-Main-Danube Canal was completed. (The Vistula and Elbe were already linked by canal to the Rhine.) The idea for making this link had been around since the time of Charlemagne (742–814). Look for the German city of Nürnberg in your atlas. It is located on the canal. Draw in the canal on your map. Highlight it in red. What might be the effect of this Rhine-Main-Danube Canal on the cities along the Danube system?

_____

_____

_____

# Eastern Europe

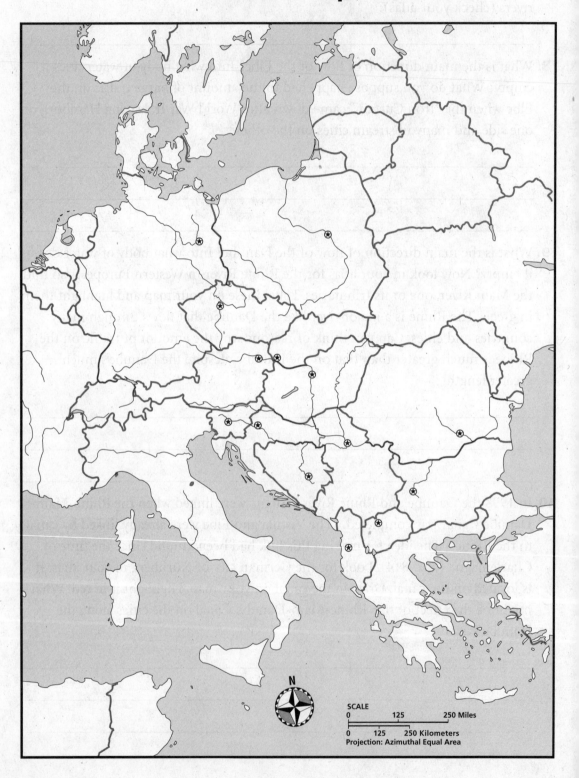

SCALE

0        125        250 Miles

0    125    250 Kilometers

Projection: Azimuthal Equal Area

**Eastern Europe**                    Critical Thinking

# Ethnic Cleansing in Bosnia

*The Balkan Peninsula in southeastern Europe has long been a region of rich culture and diversity. It has also been a place of frequent conflict and unrest. The origins of World War I in the early 1900s can be found here. More recently, violence broke out again in the region in the early 1990s, as the nation of Yugoslavia broke up. To learn more about how these events affected the people of one small Balkan country, study the information below and answer the questions that follow.*

Part of the Turkish Ottoman Empire for some 400 years, Bosnia and Herzegovina (also called Bosnia) became a state in the new nation of Yugoslavia that was created after World War I. It was an ethnically diverse region, peopled by large numbers of Serbs (who were largely Orthodox Christians), Croats (who were largely Catholic Christians), and Slavs (who were largely Muslims). Trouble erupted early in 1991 when Croatia, the state on Bosnia's western border, declared its independence. The nation's army, which was based in Serbia, Bosnia's neighbor on the east, crossed through Bosnia to regain control of Croatia. When Bosnian Croats tried to prevent the largely Serb army from moving into Croatia, fighting began.

The conflict deepened in late 1991. Bosnia's Muslim president, fearful that Serbia and Croatia intended to divide Bosnia between them, declared Bosnia's independence. Bosnian Serbs objected and a three-way civil war began in Bosnia. Its Muslim, Croat, and Serb populations all fought for territory and control of the country. Backed by neighboring Serbia, Bosnian Serbs quickly gained the upper hand in the fighting. They began a practice known as "ethnic cleansing"—mainly against the Muslims. This involved the removal, or "cleansing" of the Muslim population from all territory that came under Bosnian Serb control. Thousands of Muslims were killed and hundreds of thousands were forced to leave their homes and relocate elsewhere.

In 1994 Bosnia's Muslims and Croats settled their differences and formed a joint Muslim-Croat region within Bosnia. Additional peace accords signed the following year recognized this agreement and set up a separate Bosnia Serb state in the rest of the country. A United Nations force, led by U.S. troops and those of other NATO nations, took up positions in Bosnia to enforce the agreement, the borders, and the peace. A UN war crimes commission was created to uncover and bring to justice those responsible for the atrocities of ethnic cleansing.

The map and table on this page show the effects of the war on the people of Bosnia and Herzegovina.

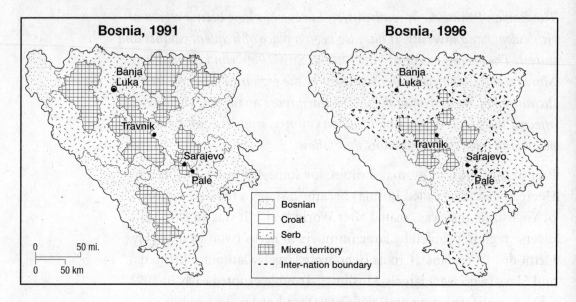

## Population Changes in Bosnia

| Year | Population | Distribution | | |
|------|-----------|--------|------|-------|
| | | Muslim | Serb | Croat |
| 1991 | 4.4 million | 44% | 33% | 17% |
| 1995 | 3.2 million | 38% | 40% | 22% |
| 1999 | 3.4 million | 38% | 40% | 22% |

**1.** What ethnic group gained the most territory in Bosnia from 1991 to 1996?

_____

**2.** What group held the largest amount of land in Bosnia in 1991? In 1996?

_____

**3.** According to these maps, how did settlement patterns change in Bosnia between 1991 and 1996?

_____

**4.** How did the population of Bosnia change between 1991 and 1995? Explain why.

_____

**5.** What evidence of ethnic cleansing in Bosnia do the map and table provide?

_____

**Eastern Europe**

# Understanding Problems and Solutions

Identifying a problem that a writer presents is important. It allows you
to better understand the solution offered—or to figure out your own
solution if one is not suggested. Review each section of your textbook
chapter. Identify one problem addressed in each section. Then write
how the problem was solved. If no solution was offered, provide your
own possible solution to the problem.

## PREREADING

**1. Identifying a Problem** Eastern Europe has faced many challenges in the past few
decades: civil war, political upheaval, revolution, accidents, and economic hard-
ship. As you review each section, choose one specific problem and write it in the
chart below.

| Section | Problem | Solution |
|---------|---------|----------|
| One | | |
| Two | | |
| Three | | |
| Four | | |

## READING

**2. Identify a Solution** Sometimes a solution is clearly explained after a problem has been presented. Other times, a solution may not be presented at all. As you read, write down a solution for each problem you recorded in the chart above. If no solution to the problem is offered in the chapter, write your own possible solution to the problem. Remember, a problem can have more than one solution.

## USING THE PROBLEM-SOLUTION STRATEGY

**3. Understanding Problems and Solutions** Identify a problem facing an Eastern European country today. In the space below, describe the problem, then offer at least two possible solutions for that problem.

_____

_____

_____

_____

_____

_____

_____

_____

**Central Asia**                                    Focus on Viewing

# Presenting and Viewing Visual Reports

Now that you have read and learned about the countries of Eastern
Europe, you will choose one country about which you will present an
oral and visual report to your classmates. Your oral report will include
facts about the history, culture, government, climate, resources, and
economy of your selected country. You will also create a poster
illustrating important geographical features of your selected country.
After presenting, you will view other students' reports and offer them
constructive feedback.

## PLANNING

**1. Presenting Physical Geography** Review your focus on viewing notes to help you
decide which country you will choose for your report. Remember that you will
include information about physical geography in your oral report, as well as
illustrations of physical features on your poster.

**2. Considering Poland and the Baltics** Does Poland or one of the Baltic countries
appeal to you for your report? If so, organize your focus on viewing notes to
decide what important facts you will include in your oral report and poster.

**3. Picturing Inland Eastern Europe** For whichever country you decide to report on,
you will need to include several pictures on the poster that accompanies your oral
presentation. Make a list of geographical features you think your audience would
find most interesting. Remember to include both physical and human features.

**4. Choosing a Country** It is time to choose the Eastern European country for your
report. Use your focus on viewing notes to help you decide. Once you select a
country, make a list of facts and illustrations you will include in your report.

## PREPARING

**5. Preparing Your Oral Report** Use the list you created in Step 4 to plan and
organize your oral presentation. You may wish to write notes on index cards,
but be careful not to read your presentation. It is important to have eye contact
with your audience members as you present. Practice your oral report out loud
to a friend. Remember to speak loudly and clearly when you present.

**6. Creating Your Poster** Use the lists you created in Steps 3 and 4 to organize and
create your poster. You may draw original illustrations or include pictures from
books and the Internet. Your poster should provide visual support for your oral
presentation. Include only pictures on the poster that you describe in your oral
report. Make sure your poster is colorful, neat, and attractive.

## PRESENTING

**7. Giving Your Oral Report**  As you give your speech to the class, keep in mind the following techniques to help make your presentation more effective.

- Approach the room with confidence.
- Look at the audience as you speak, with only occasional glances at your notes.
- Speak loudly and clearly so the audience members can hear and understand you easily.
- Ignore outside distractions, such as voices in the hallway, papers being shuffled, etc.
- Refer to your poster when talking about features that are illustrated there.

## VIEWING

**8. Viewing and Critiquing Your Classmates' Presentations**  Use the guidelines below to help you critique your classmates' presentations.

- Pay attention during the presentation so you can offer constructive feedback.
- Be respectful and kind when offering feedback.
- Include at least one strength and one weakness.
- Be specific. For example, avoid making general statements like "You did a good job." Instead say, "You did a good job making eye contact with the audience."
- Offer feedback on their oral reports, as well as their posters.

## EVALUATING

**9. Evaluating Your Presentation**  Use the questions below to evaluate your own presentation.

- Did your presentation capture and maintain your audience's interest?
- Did your presentation include information about both physical and human geographical features in your selected country?
- Did your poster provide visual support for your oral presentation? Did you refer to your poster while you were presenting?
- Did you make eye contact with your audience while presenting?
- Did you speak loudly and clearly with a confident tone?

**Eastern Europe**                                    # Chapter Review

> **BIG IDEAS**
>
> **1.** The physical geography of Eastern Europe varies greatly from place to place.
>
> **2.** The histories of Poland and the Baltic Republics, both as free states and as areas dominated by the Soviet Union, still shape life there.
>
> **3.** The countries of inland Eastern Europe have varied histories and cultures but face many of the same issues today.
>
> **4.** Life in the Balkans reflects the region's troubled past and its varied ethnic makeup.

## REVIEWING VOCABULARY, TERMS, AND PLACES

Using the clues provided, fill in the letter blanks with the correct term.

**1.** the longest river in Eastern Europe

__ __ __ __ __ __

**2.** a nuclear power plant in the Ukraine that exploded in 1986

__ __ __ __ __ __ __ __ __ __

**3.** the effort to remove all members of a group from a country

__ __ __ __ __ __   __ __ __ __ __ __ __ __

**4.** a country's resources, like roads and factories that it needs to support economic activity

__ __ __ __ __ __ __ __ __ __ __ __ __ __ __

**5.** the capital of the Czech Republic

__ __ __ __ __ __

**6.** the capital of Hungary

__ __ __ __ __ __ __ __

**7.** low mountains that stretch in a long arc from the Alps to the Black Sea area

__ __ __ __ __ __ __ __ __ __ __ __

**8.** the capital of Poland

__ __ __ __ __ __ __

Eastern Europe, *continued*                                    Chapter Review

## COMPREHENSION AND CRITICAL THINKING

Read each **FALSE** sentence below. On the line provided, replace the underlined word or words to make the statement **TRUE**.

1. The <u>Baltic</u> Peninsula is one of the largest peninsulas in Europe.

   _____

2. The <u>infrastructure</u> is an international union in Eastern Europe that meets about issues such as trade and immigration.

   _____

3. In the 800s, a group called the Rus built a settlement in what is now <u>Prague</u>.

   _____

## REVIEWING THEMES

In the space provided, explain how each term is related to the geography theme.

1. **Theme: region**

   Communist government _____

   _____

2. **Theme: human-environment interaction**

   industrial centers _____

   _____

## REVIEW ACTIVITY: BUSINESS PLAN

You are a successful businessperson and have been asked to help revitalize the economy in one of the Eastern European countries. Choose a country in Eastern Europe, then come up with three ideas that would help that country's economy grow. Explain why you think your business plan will work.

Teacher's Interdisciplinary Project

# Research Project: Eastern Europe's Economy

## OVERVIEW/PURPOSE

Students will work in groups to research different aspects of Eastern Europe's economy. Each group will present their findings to the rest of the class.

## PLANNING

### Time Suggested

Three one-hour blocks and one week of outside class time for research

### Materials

- large paper (white or light-colored for background, colored construction paper)
- colored pencils or markers, scissors, glue
- Student Handout 1: "Industrial Economy"
- Student Handout 2: "Tourist Economy"
- Student Handout 3: "Business Plans: Improve the Economy"
- Rubric: "Standards for Evaluating Your Work"

### Resources

http://www.cia.gov/cia/publications/factbook/

Gros, Daniel and Steinherr, Alfred. *Winds of Change: Economic Transition in Central and Eastern Europe.* Addison Wesley Longman, 1995.

### Preparation

Schedule library time for research.

### Group Size

Students will divide into three groups.

## OBJECTIVES

- Research a specific aspect of the economy in three Eastern European countries in the past five years—industry OR tourism.

- Create and present a report with supporting visuals of the industrial economy or tourist economy of the three countries chosen. As part of the report, each group will estimate, using sources, how much the countries earned each year and estimate that country's economic earnings over a five-year period.

- Brainstorm ideas for how each country can further improve their economies.

## PROCEDURE

1. Discuss with students different ways that the economy of countries in Eastern Europe is impacted by industry and tourism.

2. Have students review their textbook chapter and brainstorm examples of industries in Eastern Europe. Have them do the same for major tourist areas in Eastern Europe.

3. Divide students into three groups and have each group choose any Eastern European country covered in the textbook chapter to research. Make sure each group has selected a different country.

4. Distribute copies of **Handout 1: Industrial Economy, Handout 2: Tourist Economy,** and **Handout 3: Business Plans: Improve the Economy** to each student. Instruct students to use the information on these handouts as well as the Internet and library books to learn more about the economy of the country their group selected. Ask the librarian for help in selecting materials that will aid students in their research.

5. Tell students to follow the project guidelines on their handouts to plan, organize, and present a business plan explaining how to improve the economy in their selected country. Use **Rubric: Standards for Evaluating Your Work** to evaluate each group's presentation.

## EXTEND

Ask students to research other ways, besides industry and tourism, that Eastern European countries could improve their economies. Have students create a brochure that explains and illustrates their findings.

**Eastern Europe**

# Interdisciplinary Project
## Research Project: Eastern Europe's Economy

# Industrial Economy

### WHAT IS AN INDUSTRY?

An industry is a large-scale business activity. It often involves manufacturing a product, but it can also involve a service. Some examples of industry are furniture-making, film production, and agriculture.

### INDUSTRY IN EASTERN EUROPE

Each person in your group will gather information about the various industries in the country your group selected. While you conduct research, you should look for:

- the main industries in your country
- how many people these industries employ
- economic predictions (growth or decline) of the industries
- how much money each industry earned for your country last year
- how much money each industry earned for your country in the past five years (total)

### PROJECT REQUIREMENTS

Your group's presentation should include the following:

- a description of your country's main industries
- the general location of each of your country's main industries
- explanation of how the industry got started in those locations
- general predictions (growth or decline) of the industries
- table, chart, or other visual showing how much income the industry earned in one year
- table, chart, or other visual showing how much income the industry earned — in the past five years
- the names and roles of all group members

Name _____ Class _____ Date _____

**Eastern Europe**

# Interdisciplinary Project

## Research Project: Eastern Europe's Economy

# Tourist Economy

### WHAT IS TOURISM?

Tourism is when people travel to an area for recreation and to enjoy that area's culture and environment. Many parts of Eastern Europe rely heavily on tourism to support the economy.

### TOURISM IN EASTERN EUROPE

Each person in your group will gather information about the various tourist attractions in the country your group selected. While you conduct research, you should look for:

- the main tourist attractions in your country
- how many people tourism employs
- economic predictions (growth or decline) of tourism
- how much money tourism earned for your country last year
- how much money tourism earned for your country in the past five years (total)

### PROJECT REQUIREMENTS

Your group's presentation should include the following:

- a description of each tourist attraction
- the location of each tourist attraction
- explanation of how tourism got started in those locations
- general predictions (growth or decline) of tourism
- table, chart, or other visual showing how much income tourism earned in one year
- table, chart, or other visual showing how much income tourism earned in the past five years
- an image of each tourist attraction or destination
- the names and roles of all group members

**Europe and Russia**

**Eastern Europe**                    Interdisciplinary Project

### Research Project: Eastern Europe's Economy

# Business Plans: Improve the Economy

Eastern Europe's economy suffered when it transitioned away from Communism. Even though progress is being made in some areas, the countries are still seeking other sources of income. Based on your research, present two business ideas that would help stimulate the economy.

## BUSINESS PLAN

Each person in your group will gather information about how industry and tourism can be improved in the country your group selected. While you conduct research, you should look for:

- reasons why industry and tourism are or are not currently succeeding in the country your group selected

- new ideas for other industries or tourist destinations that the area could support

- ways other countries earn income through industry and tourism

## PROJECT REQUIREMENTS

Your group's presentation should include the following:

- two ways that industry and tourism could improve in the country your group selected

- two new ideas for other industries or tourist destinations that the area could support

- table, chart, or other visual showing your ideas for economic improvement

- the names and roles of all group members

**Eastern Europe**

# Interdisciplinary Project

## Research Project: Eastern Europe's Economy

# Standards for Evaluating Your Work

### EXCELLENT

- The presentation includes all required information.
- The presentation is well researched and clearly presented.
- The visuals are well organized, neat, attractive, and well made.
- The project includes the names and roles of all group members.

### GOOD

- The presentation includes most of the required information.
- The presentation shows research and is clearly presented.
- The visuals are organized, neat, and adequately made.
- The project includes the names and roles of most group members.

### ACCEPTABLE

- The presentation includes some of the required information.
- The presentation shows evidence of research and is clearly presented, but it needs more supporting facts and editing.
- The visuals are somewhat organized and fairly well made.
- The project includes the names and roles of some group members.

### UNACCEPTABLE

- The presentation is missing significant amounts of required information.
- The presentation is poorly researched, poorly presented, and contains factual errors or lacks supporting details.
- The visuals are poorly organized and poorly made.
- The project is missing the names and roles of group members.

**Russia and the Caucasus**

# Vocabulary Builder

## Section 1

| | | |
|---|---|---|
| Caspian Sea | Caucasus Mountains | Moscow |
| Siberia | taiga | Ural Mountains |
| Volga River | steppe | |

**DIRECTIONS** Read each sentence and fill in the blank with the word in the word pair that best completes the sentence.

1. The _____ form the northern border between the Causcasus region and Russia. (**Caucasus Mountains/Ural Mountains**)

2. It is in the _____ that the continents of Europe and Asia meet. (**Caucasus Mountains/Ural Mountains**)

3. The _____ provides an important transportation route through Russia. (**Caspian Sea/Volga River**)

4. The _____'s rich, black soil has made it Russia's main farming area. (**steppe/taiga**)

5. _____ is a cold, empty land of barren plains and endless forests. (**Siberia/Moscow**)

**DIRECTIONS** Choose four of the terms from the word bank. On a separate sheet of paper, use these words to write a story or poem that relates to the section.

# Russia and the Caucasus

## Vocabulary Builder

### Section 2

| | | |
|---|---|---|
| Bolsheviks | Cold War | communism |
| Cyrillic | czar | gulags |
| Kiev | propaganda | reaction |

**DIRECTIONS** Look at each set of four terms. On the line provided, write the letter of the term that does not relate to the others.

_____ **1. a.** Cyrillic    **b.** Stalin    **c.** communism    **d.** gulags

_____ **2. a.** Cold War    **b.** weapons    **c.** Bolsheviks    **d.** arms race

_____ **3. a.** communism    **b.** propaganda    **c.** Soviet Union    **d.** czar

_____ **4. a.** Vikings    **b.** Bolsheviks    **c.** Kiev    **d.** Rus

_____ **5. a.** Ivan IV    **b.** czar    **c.** Catherine the Great    **d.** Kiev

**DIRECTIONS** Choose five of the terms from the word bank. Use these words to write a summary of what you learned in the section.

_____

_____

_____

_____

_____

_____

_____

_____

_____

_____

_____

_____

_____

**Russia and the Caucasus**

# Vocabulary Builder

## Section 3

| | | |
|---|---|---|
| Chechnya | smelters | dachas |
| St. Petersburg | Sea of Okhotsk | Trans-Siberian Railroad |

**DIRECTIONS** Read each sentence and fill in the blank with the word in the word pair that best completes the sentence.

**1.** Located on the Gulf of Finland, _____ has been called the Venice of the North for its many canals. (**Chechnya/St. Petersburg**)

**2.** In the Ural Mountains, factories called _____ process the copper and iron that is mined in the region. (**dachas/smelters**)

**DIRECTIONS** On the line provided before each statement, write **T** if a statement is true and **F** if a statement is false. If the statement is false, write the correct term on the line after each sentence that makes the sentence a true statement.

_____ **3.** Cities and towns in Siberia are mostly located near the Sea of Okhotsk.

_____

_____ **4.** Wealthy Russians go to their dachas to enjoy outdoor activities.

_____

_____ **5.** Ethnic conflict is responsible for fighting in St. Petersburg.

_____

**Russia and the Caucasus**　　　　　Vocabulary Builder

**Section 4**

| agrarian | Armenia | Azerbaijan | Baku |
|---|---|---|---|
| Black Sea | Caspian Sea | Tbilisi | Yerevan |

**DIRECTIONS** Write three words or phrases that describe each term.

**1.** agrarian _____

**2.** Baku _____

**DIRECTIONS** Read each sentence and fill in the blank with the word in the word pair that best completes the sentence.

**3.** The capital of Armenia is _____. **(Baku/Yerevan)**

**4.** _____ is the capital of Georgia. **(Yerevan/Tbilisi)**

**5.** Oil is the most important part of _____'s economy. **(Armenia/Azerbaijan)**

**6.** After World War I, _____, Azerbaijan, and Georgia became part of the Soviet Union. **(Chechnya/Armenia)**

**7.** The _____ draws tourists to Georgia each year. **(Caspian Sea/Black Sea)**

　　　　　Europe and Russia

**Russia and the Caucasus**

Biography

# Catherine the Great
## 1729-1796

**HOW SHE AFFECTED THE REGION** Under Catherine the Great's rule, the Russian Empire grew. Although she believed in the ideas of the Enlightenment, Catherine ruled with a strong hand. Although she made many reforms to improve life in Russia, she did not free Russia's serfs, keeping them tied to their owners' lands.

© Bridgeman Art Library

*As you read the biography below, think about how Catherine the Great's leadership helped modernize Russia.*

Catherine the Great was born a German princess in the city of Stettin, Germany, which is now part of Poland. Her name at birth was Sophie. When Sophie was 14, Czarina Elizabeth, Empress of Russia, chose her to marry Peter, the **successor** to Russia's throne.

Sophie changed her name to Catherine and converted to the Russian Orthodox religion. Catherine was very intelligent and hard-working. She quickly learned the Russian language. Catherine also grew to love Russia very dearly. It was not long, however, before her marriage failed.

Catherine greatly disliked how her husband Peter ruled Russia after Czarina Elizabeth died. Peter had made an **alliance** with Prussia, long an enemy of Russia. He made other decisions that also hurt Russia. Catherine decided that Russia would be better served if she ruled, not Peter. She knew that her love for Russia had gained her the support of much of Russian society, including Russia's army. In 1762, Catherine led the army against Peter and

**VOCABULARY**

**successor** one who is named to be the next ruler

**alliance** a treaty or agreement to join together

**ceased** stopped, ended

**dependent** greatly in need of, could not exist without

Europe and Russia

removed him from the throne. She took over as
Empress of Russia, calling herself Catherine II.

During her rule, she greatly expanded the Russian
Empire. Catherine added over 200,000 square miles
of territory to Russia. She also worked hard to keep
Russia out of Europe's wars. However, she also
helped to divide up Poland among Russia, Prussia,
and Austria. As a result, Poland **ceased** to exist as
a country.

Catherine was well-read, and she communicated
with many of the great minds of the Enlightenment.
Although she wanted to free Russia's serfs, she
decided not to do so. She needed the support of
Russia's nobles—who were **dependent** on the serfs
for their wealth.

A lover of the arts, Catherine built new museums,
libraries, and even towns throughout Russia. She
also created the first Russian schools for girls and
a medical college. Catherine died in 1796, having
earned the title of Catherine the Great for her legacy
of reform, expansion, and education.

## WHAT DID YOU LEARN?

**1. Recall**  What were some of Catherine the Great's accomplishments?

_____

_____

**2. Expressing and Supporting a Point of View**  Do you think Catherine did the right
thing by overthrowing her husband to become Empress? Why or why not?

_____

_____

## ACTIVITY

Imagine that Catherine the Great chose you to be her successor to the
Russian throne. What advice would you ask of her and why? On a
separate sheet of paper, write three questions you would ask her and
the answers you think she would give.

**Russia and the Caucasus**                    Biography

# Garry Kasparov
## 1963-

**HOW HE AFFECTED THE WORLD** Garry Kasparov started playing chess at the age of six and became the youngest world champion chess player ever when he was just 22. Kasparov remained the top chess player for 20 years before turning to politics.

*As you read the biography below,* think about how Garry Kasparov's determination helped him become the world's best chess player for many years.

Reuters/CORBIS

**VOCABULARY**

**republic** similar to a state in the United States or a province in Canada

**draws** games that end in a tie, or with no clear winner

Garry Kasparov was born in Baku, Azerbaijan. His father was Jewish and his mother was Armenian. At the time, Azerbaijan was a **republic** of the Soviet Union. Kasparov began to learn how to play chess when he was only six years old.

When Kasparov was 10 years old, he studied at the top Soviet chess school. He went on to win the Soviet Junior Championship at age 13. By age 16, Kasparov had won his first international tournament. Still a teen, he was now eager to take on the best chess players in the world. However, partly due to Soviet politics, Kasparov was not able to challenge the top player of the world, Anatoly Karpov, for a few years. Karpov—also from the Soviet Union—was the favorite of Soviet leaders.

Finally, in 1984, Kasparov met Karpov in the world championship. The match lasted for 48 games and took six months—the longest in the history of chess. With no clear winner, officials stopped the match and ordered a rematch. A year later Kasparov won a 24-game rematch. At the age of 22 he had become the youngest world chess champion.

Kasparov continued as world chess champion for
15 more years, until losing his crown in 2000. He
retired in 2005, after failing to regain the title of
world chess champion.

One of Kasparov's boldest moves came in 1996.
That was when he competed in a six-game chess
match against Deep Blue, a powerful IBM computer
specially-built to win at chess. Kasparov defeated
Deep Blue, winning three games, losing one, and two
ending in **draws**. However, in a 1997 rematch with
an updated version of the computer, Kasparov lost.

After Kasparov's retirement in 2005, he turned
his attention to Russian politics.

## WHAT DID YOU LEARN?

1. **Explain** How did Garry Kasparov become world chess champion?

   _____

   _____

2. **Make an Inference** Do you think playing a game against a computer is easier or
   harder than playing against a person? Why?

   _____

   _____

## ACTIVITY

Have you ever played chess? Research an aspect of chess that interests
you, such as the game's history, what the pieces and game board were
made of in the past and what they are made of today, and how chess is
played around the world. Write a short paper about your findings. Then
find a partner and play a game of chess.

# *War and Peace*
## by Leo Tolstoy

**ABOUT THE READING** Considered one of Russia's greatest novels, *War and Peace* takes place in the early 1800s. The story is complex, following three families over a difficult period in Russia's history—when France's Napoleon tried to take over Russia.

**VOCABULARY**
**turrets** small towers
**perished** died
**strewn** littered
**adjutant** a staff officer

*As you read the passage below,* pay attention to the descriptions of the battlefield and the emotions that the character Rostov experiences.

Rostov rode on . . . not knowing why or to whom he was now going. The <u>Emperor</u> was wounded, the battle lost. It was impossible to doubt it now. Rostov rode in the direction pointed out to him, in which he saw **turrets** and a church. What need to hurry? What was he now to say to the <u>Tsar or to Kutuzov</u>, even if they were alive and unwounded?

> The Emperor is Francis of Austria, who had joined with Russia's Czar Alexander to fight against Napoleon. Kutuzov is a Russian general.

"Take this road, your honor, that way you will be killed at once!" a soldier shouted to him. "They'd kill you there!"

"Oh, what are you talking about?" said another. "Where is he to go? That way is nearer."

Rostov considered, and then went in the direction where they said he would be killed.

"It's all the same now. If the Emperor is wounded, am I to try to save myself?" he thought. He rode on to the region where the greatest number of men had **perished** . . . All about the field, like heaps of manure on well-kept plowland, lay from ten to fifteen dead and wounded to each couple of acres. The wounded crept together in twos and threes and one could hear their distressing screams and groans . . . He put his horse to the trot to avoid seeing all these suffering men, and he felt afraid—afraid not for his life, but for the courage he needed and which he knew would not stand the sight of these unfortunates.

> Underline the word that describes Rostov's feelings as he rides through the battlefield.

The French, who had ceased firing at this field **strewn** with dead and wounded where there was no one left to fire at, on seeing an **adjutant** riding over it trained a gun on him and fired several shots. The sensation of those terrible whistling sounds and of the corpses around him merged in Rostov's mind into a single feeling of terror and pity for himself. He remembered his mother's last letter.

"What would she feel," thought he, "if she saw me now on this field with the cannon aimed at me?"

## ANALYZING LITERATURE

**1. Main Ideas** Why does Rostov experience such strong feelings as he rides through the battlefield?

_____

_____

**2. Critical Thinking: Analyzing** Do you think Tolstoy was pro-war or anti-war, based on this passage? Why?

_____

_____

_____

## ACTIVITY

Obtain a copy of *War and Peace* from your school or public library. Read another short passage from it. Write an essay that compares and contrasts the main ideas or characters from each passage.

**Russia and the Caucasus**                    Primary Source

# Russian Icon Painting

**ABOUT THE SOURCE** The tradition of icon painting began in Byzantium, where early icons were often created as mosaics or painted panels. Russian icon paintings were usually done on wood. They were not intended to be realistic images. Instead, Russian icon paintings were meant to help people—most of whom could not read—better understand the New Testament of the Christian Bible and aid in prayer.

*As you look at the icon painting,* note the way your eyes move around the picture. Why do you think Russian icon painters wanted viewers to do this?

© Bildarchiv Preussischer Kulurbesitz/Art Resource, NY

## WHAT DID YOU LEARN?

**1. Explain**  Why do you think icons were important in Russian Orthodox churches?

_____

_____

_____

**2. Describe**  How would you describe the style of the Russian icon painting on the previous page to someone who had not seen it?

_____

_____

_____

**3. Draw Conclusions**  Today, the word *icon* is often used to mean a symbol that stands for, or represents, something else. For example, the little pictures—icons— that you see on computer monitors may stand for a folder, file, or software application. Why do you think icons are used today?

_____

_____

_____

# Serfdom in Russia, 1860

By 1860, there were over 20 million serfs in Russia—and almost half of all adult males were serfs. Russian serfs were tied to the land, having to pay rent or provide labor to their landlords. Because of serfdom, the Russian economy was considered somewhat backward. After growing unrest by serfs throughout Russia, Czar Alexander II granted them freedom in 1861. He hoped that freeing the serfs would help Russia become a more modern country. It did, but the Czar's act also helped fuel forces that resulted in the Russian Revolution of 1917.

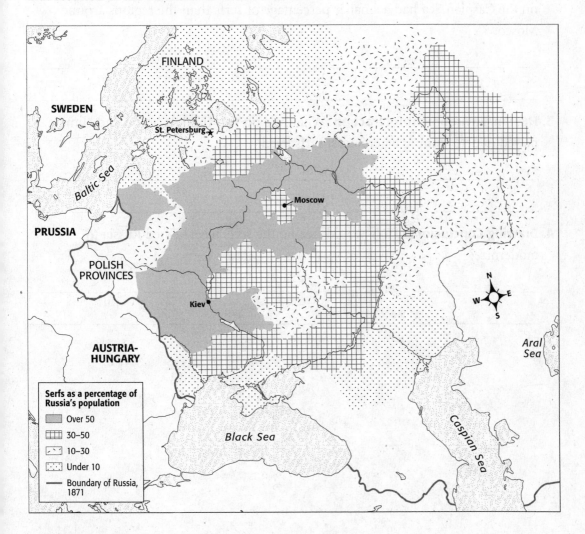

**Serfs as a percentage of Russia's population**

- ▓ Over 50
- ▦ 30–50
- ▨ 10–30
- ░ Under 10
- ── Boundary of Russia, 1871

## MAP ACTIVITY

**1.** Color the areas with over 50 red.

**2.** Color the areas with 30–50 orange.

**3.** Color the areas with 10–30 yellow.

**4.** Color the areas with under 10 blue.

## ANALYZING MAPS

**1. Regions** Why do you think the Moscow region had a greater percentage of serfs than the St. Petersburg region?

_____

_____

**2. Location** Why do you think Finland (ruled by Russia at the time) and the region on the Caspian Sea had a smaller percentage of serfs than the regions around Moscow?

_____

_____

**3. Human/Environment Interaction** What role do you think location and climate played in determining where most serfs lived?

_____

_____

**4. Drawing Conclusions** How would freeing the serfs have helped Russia to modernize?

_____

_____

**Russia and the Caucasus**

# Social Studies Skills

## Geography

# Interpreting a Population Map

**LEARN THE SKILL**

Some population maps show you what percentage a group makes up of
the total population in a region or country. For example, on the map
below, children under 15 years old make up 16 to 18 percent of the
Moscow region's total population. That means, nearly one in five people
in the Moscow region is 15 or under.

**PRACTICE THE SKILL**

Study the map below and answer the questions that follow.

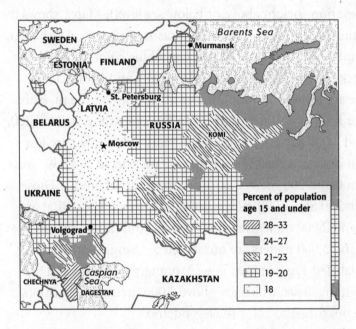

**1.** What percent of the Chechen region do those 15 and under make up?

_____

**2.** Which of these three regions—Murmansk, Dagastan, or Komi—has the smallest
percent of people 15 and under living in it?

_____

**3.** Why do you think the more urban regions on the map, such as Moscow, have a
smaller percent of young people than other regions in Russia?

_____

_____

Geography for Life

# Agriculture and Environment in the Caucasus

Many factors influence what a farmer grows. Cultural traditions are
important. Farmers often produce what has "always" been produced
in their area. Demand and prices are also important considerations. If
a farmer is part of a market system, he or she must ask, "Can I make a
profit growing this crop at this place?" Government agricultural policies
and assistance play a big role in some parts of the world. The physical
environment is also a key factor.

## YOU ARE THE GEOGRAPHER

Color Map 1 on the next page. When you are done, it will show six
categories of elevation (height above or below sea level). Map 1 shows the
boundaries of the three countries in the Caucasus (Armenia, Azerbaijan,
and Georgia) and land-water boundaries. Use a blue colored pencil to
color in the Black Sea, the Caspian Sea, Lake Sevan, and Mingechaur
Reservoir (these are labeled on Map 2). The other lines on the map are
contour lines, or lines of equal elevation. On this map, they are at 0, 200,
1,000, 2,000, and 3,000 meters. On the map, areas of land that are less
than 0 meters in elevation (below sea level) are numbered 1. Those areas
that are between 0 and 200 meters in elevation are numbered 2. Those
that are between 200 and 1,000 meters are numbered 3. Those that are
between 1,000 and 2,000 meters are numbered 4, and those that are
between 2,000 and 3,000 meters are numbered 5. Using colored pencils,
color the areas labeled 1, green; 2, yellow; 3, orange; 4, brown; and 5,
black. The remaining areas, which are above 3,000 meters in elevation,
leave white. Do not forget to color the legend, too.

Now that you have colored Map 1, you can see the Great Caucasus
Mountains along the northern edge of this region (the north-facing
slope of this range is in Russia) and the Lesser Caucasus and Armenian
Plateau in the south. At the west end of the region is the Colchis
Lowland, facing the Black Sea, and in the east is the Kura Lowland,
facing the Caspian.

Topographical patterns and agricultural patterns are related for several
reasons. Topography influences soils, slope, temperature, precipitation,
and ease of access. All of these factors in turn affect what can be grown
where. When you compare the two maps, remember that temperatures
decrease with higher elevations. This is important because there are
many crops that will not grow where freezing temperatures are common
2,000 meters). Precipitation also varies in this region. In general,

Europe and Russia

there is more moisture in the west and less in the east. Samtredia, on the Colchis Lowland, gets an average of 56 inches of rain per year. Tbilisi, close to the center of the region, gets 20 inches per year. Zyud-Ostov-Kultuk, on the Kura Lowland, gets only 11 inches per year.

## Map 1: Contour Map of the Caucasus

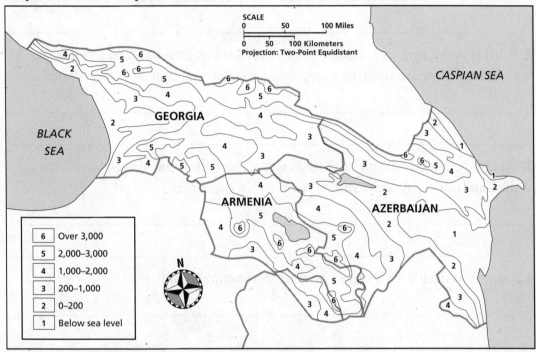

## Map 2: Agricultural Patterns of the Caucasus

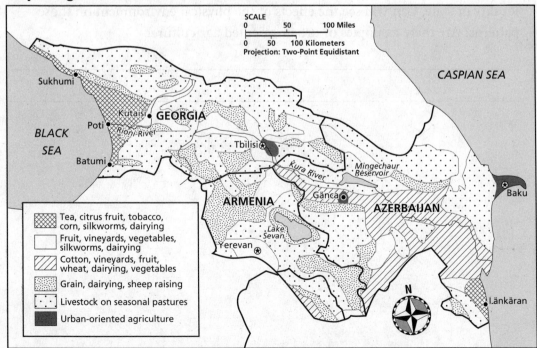

Compare Maps 1 and 2. Then answer the questions that follow.

1. What is raised in the lowland regions of the Caucasus? Why do some of the agricultural products differ between the Colchis and the Kura Lowlands? What do you think Mingechaur Reservoir has to do with agriculture?

   _____

   _____

2. What types of agriculture dominate in the medium-elevation areas of the Caucasus? How are vines, tree crops, and animals well suited to steep slopes?

   _____

   _____

3. What type of agricultural use is the most important in the highest elevations of the Caucasus? Why are pastures "seasonal" in these areas?

   _____

   _____

4. Around which places is urban-oriented agriculture found?

   _____

   _____

5. Finish this exercise with a group discussion of agricultural patterns in your locality or state. Can you see the effects of the physical environment on those patterns? Are there examples of urban-oriented agriculture?

   _____

   _____

**Russia and the Caucasus**                    # Critical Thinking

# A Russian Space Mystery

Scientists are still trying to find an explanation for an extraterrestrial event that occurred in Russia nearly a century ago and that has puzzled the world since. To learn more about this event and efforts to unlock its secrets, study the following passage and answer the questions that follow.

On June 30, 1908, a vast fireball raced through the dawn sky over Siberia, then exploded with the force of 1,000 Hiroshima bombs . . . For days, and for thousands of miles around, the sky remained bright with an eerie orange glow—as far away as western Europe people were able to read newspapers at night without a lamp. The effect was much like that of a giant volcanic eruption, yet there had been no eruption . . .

Scientists did not come to Tunguska [in Siberia] for . . . 19 years, apparently reluctant to travel to a site so swampy and remote. When they did finally come, they were rewarded with a stunning vision of utter devastation, with scorched trees lying in rows that stretched to the horizon. They searched for a crater but found none. They searched for fragments of a meteorite—an asteroid or chunk of one—but found none. All they found were eyewitnesses in neighboring villages who told of a fireball streaking through the sky, horrifying noise, and a blast that knocked people off their feet. Clearly something unprecedented [never seen before] had occurred at Tunguska, but the trees were the only tangible proof that remained.

. . . Not until the late fifties would scientists visit Tunguska again. The prod [reason] would be Alexander Kazantsev, a Soviet engineer and an army colonel who in 1946 wrote a short story in which he suggested that only a nuclear explosion could have caused the bizarre wreckage at Tunguska . . . and . . . [that] it must have been caused by an exploding spaceship . . .

For three decades Tunguska remained an exclusively Russian scientific investigation . . . In 1989, with the end of the cold war, outside researchers were at last able to begin studying the site. Among them was the Italian physicist Menotti Galli . . . Galli has studied phenomena associated with cosmic radiation, including the possibility that high-energy particles from space can add heavy isotopes of carbon to the cellulose in trees. And it is in trees he realized, and particularly in their annual growth rings, that an answer to the Tunguska mystery might be hiding . . . If a Tunguska bolide [object from space] had showered any particles into the forest, they would have been trapped in the [tree ring] resin and might still be intact . . .

The Italians found six spruces . . . that had survived the blast. They gouged out 13 core samples the size of healthy carrots . . . The results were striking: . . . A significant number of particles had unusually high levels of elements like copper, gold, and nickel. Because many of these elements have a relatively high number of protons (denoted by physicists as Z), the researchers dubbed [named] the particles that contain them "high-Z particles." There were 10 times more high-Z particles [in tree ring resin] in the period of the fireball than before or after, which made the Italians wonder if these particles had an extra-Earthly origin . . .

American researchers have been creating computer simulations of Tunguska, trying to . . . re-create a bolide that could have produced the known evidence . . . Small bolides burn up quickly in our atmosphere, while huge ones reach the ground. But when a midsize bolide (between 10 and 300 feet wide) falls, the researchers found, something different happens. As the bolide rips through the atmosphere, the air exerts intense pressure on its front end . . . However, there's practically no pressure being applied to the back of the bolide . . . The huge difference in forces acting on different areas of the object . . . turns the bolide into a cloud of debris, looking as if it had been dynamited in midair . . . A 200-foot-wide stony meteorite falling to Earth at a 45-degree angle would explode at exactly the right height over Tunguska. Moreover, such an event could also explain the "light nights". . . that followed the explosion: the force of the blast wave, . . . the [computer] model suggests, lofted [threw] dust into the upper atmosphere high enough to reflect light from the sun long after it had set.

From "The Last Great Impact on Earth" (retitled "A Russian Space Mystery") by Richard Stone from *Discover*, September 1996. Copyright © 1996 by **Discover Magazine.** Reproduced by permission of the publisher.

**1.** If, as the Russian engineer argued, the event at Tunguska resulted from a nuclear explosion, why would that lead to his conclusion that a spaceship was the cause?

_____

_____

**2.** What roles did geography and politics play in keeping the Tunguska event a mystery for nearly a century?

_____

_____

**Russia and the Caucasus**                     Focus on Reading

# Making Generalizations

A generalization is a broad, general conclusion drawn from examples, facts, or other information. When you make a generalization, you use details to reach a conclusion that is widely true about the given topic.

**LEARN THE SKILL**

Read the following passage.

> So far in May, London has had twelve inches of rain. Yesterday was partly cloudy, but the meteorologist is calling for rain four out of five days this week. Tourism is very slow for London this time of year.

Using the information in the passage, you could make the following generalization.

> London is rainy in May.

**PRACTICE MAKING GENERALIZATIONS**

Examine the information about the four culture regions that make up Russia's heartland in Section 3 of your textbook. These are the Moscow, St. Petersburg, Volga, and Urals regions. Use the chart below or one you create to take notes that will help guide you in making your generalizations on the next page.

| Culture Region | Fact One | Fact Two | Fact Three |
|---|---|---|---|
| Moscow | | | |
| St. Petersburg | | | |
| Volga | | | |
| Urals | | | |

Use the lines below to make one generalization about each of the four
culture regions. Remember to base your generalizations on the facts
from your chart.

Moscow _____

_____

St. Petersburg _____

_____

Volga _____

_____

Urals _____

_____

## APPLYING THE SKILL

Review the generalizations you made about each region above. Then
look for what your generalizations have in common with each other.
Use this information to write one generalization about Russia's
heartland on the lines provided.

Russia's heartland _____

_____

Choose another section from the chapter on Russia and the Caucasus.
On a separate piece of paper, make a chart like the one on the previous
page. Add facts to your chart while you review the section you chose.
Then write at least two generalizations based on your chart.

## EVALUATING YOUR GENERALIZATIONS

Use the questions below to evaluate and revise your generalizations.
### Rubric

- Do you have enough facts to make each generalization?

- Is each generalization supported by the facts on your chart?

- Is each generalization a broad statement or general conclusion?

- Is each generalization well-written?

- Is the grammar and punctuation for each generalization correct?

**Russia and the Caucasus**                    # Focus on Writing

# Creating a Real Estate Ad

You are a real estate agent, planning to sell a property in Russia or the
Caucasus. To do so, you need an ad for the newspaper and Internet.

## PREWRITING

**1. Describing the Physical Geography** Note the physical characteristics of each
   region. Also include information about climate, vegetation, and resources. List
   possible locations in both Russia and the Caucasus for the property you will sell.

**2. Considering Russia's History and Culture** Review Section 2. What could your ad
   include about the culture and history of any Russian location on your list? Write
   your ideas down on paper.

**3. Collecting Details about Russia Today** Review the information you have about
   Russia. Choose one location in Russia that would appeal to potential buyers.

**4. Collecting Details about the Caucasus** List the features of each Caucasus country that you think would appeal to potential buyers. Now choose one Caucasus
   location for the property you might sell.

## WRITING

**5. Creating a Real Estate Ad** Choose the location for the property you will sell.
   Then use the chart below to help you write your ad.

| | |
|---|---|
| **What are the location's best features?** | |
| **How would you describe the land and climate?** | |
| **How would you describe the culture, people and history?** | |
| **What are the benefits of living here?** | |
| **What does the property look like? What is nearby?** | |

**6. Completing Your Real Estate Ad** Use the information from your completed chart to write your real estate ad. Be sure to include specific details—based on facts—that will make the property attractive to potential buyers.

## EVALUATING AND PROOFREADING

**7. Evaluating Your Real Estate Ad** Does your ad give an appealing picture of the property you are trying to sell? Use the questions below to evaluate and revise your ad.

**Rubric**

- Is your ad based on facts and not misleading to potential buyers?
- Are details included about the best features of the location you chose?
- Does your ad include details that would appeal to potential buyers?
- Does your ad use descriptive wording, so potential buyers have a clear mental image of the property?

**8. Proofreading Your Real Estate Ad** Lastly, check the following:

- Capitalization and spelling of all proper names and places
- Punctuation, grammar, and spelling

# Russia and the Caucasus

## Chapter Review

**BIG IDEAS**

1. Russia is big and cold with vast plains and forests, whereas the Caucasus countries are small, mountainous, and warmer.

2. Strict rule, unrest, and ethnic diversity have shaped Russia's history and culture.

3. Russia is a federal republic with a growing market economy but faces tough challenges.

4. In an area long ruled by outside groups, the Caucasus republics are struggling to strengthen their economies and to deal with ethnic unrest and conflict.

## REVIEWING VOCABULARY, TERMS, AND PLACES

Use the description on the right to unscramble the term on the left.
Then write the term in the space provided.

| AISBREI |
|---|

1. _____ A cold, vast land of barren plains and forest

| PPESTE |
|---|

2. _____ Russia's main farming area with rich soil

| LLCCIIYR |
|---|

3. _____ A form of the Greek alphabet adopted by the Rus

| LSAGUG |
|---|

4. _____ Harsh Soviet labor camps where millions were sent

| MKLNIRE |
|---|

5. _____ The center of Russia's government in Moscow

| GALVO |
|---|

6. _____ Cultural region known for giant factories

| ISIBTIL |
|---|

7. _____ Capital of the Caucasus country bordering the Black Sea

| NIARARAG |
|---|

8. _____ A society centered around farming

## COMPREHENSION AND CRITICAL THINKING

Read each sentence below and fill in the blank with the best choice from the pair provided.

**1.** Oil is the most important part of _____'s economy. (**Armenia/Azerbaijan**)

**2.** The vast forests of the _____ cover much of Russia. (**steppe/taiga**)

**3.** _____ was Russia's first czar. (**Peter the Great/Ivan the Terrible**)

**4.** The Soviet Union became a _____ country under Lenin and Stalin. (**democratic/communist**)

**5.** The _____ is the longest single rail line in the world. (**Volga/Trans-Siberian Railroad**)

**6.** Today Russia faces _____ conflicts in some areas. (**agrarian/ethnic**)

## REVIEWING THEMES

In the space provided, explain how each term relates to the theme listed below.

   **Theme:** *movement*

**1.** Siberia _____

_____

**2.** Volga River _____

_____

## REVIEW ACTIVITY: FLASH CARDS

Skim each section of the chapter on Russia and the Caucasus. Write down at least three key terms from each section on index cards, one term per card. On the back of each card write down the term's meaning. Then use your cards to help you study. Shuffle the cards and lay them answer-side down on a table or desk. Say or write down the meaning, then turn the card over to see if you are correct. Switch cards with a classmate, and test one another with each other's cards.

# The Russian Space Program

## OVERVIEW/PURPOSE

Students will create an illustrated time line of Russia's achievements in space exploration. They will research the country's background in space flight, travel, and experimentation to discover how Russia has been a world leader in this area. Students may also compare the United States' history in space exploration with that of Russia to show how competition played a key role in how quickly various technologies were developed and perfected.

## PLANNING
### Time Suggested

Three 45-minute blocks and one week of outside class time for research

## Materials

- computers with Internet access
- library books and magazines
- large white paper that can be taped together and displayed around the room to create one large time line
- colored pencils, markers, crayons, scrap paper, scissors, and glue
- Student Handout 1: "Student Activity Outline"
- Student Handout 2: "The Importance of Space Exploration"
- Student Handout 3: "Comparing World Space Exploration"
- Rubric: "Standards for Evaluating Your Work"

## Resources

http://go.hrw.com
http://www.fas.org/spp/guide/russia
*Off the Planet: Surviving Five Perilous Months Aboard the Space Station MIR* by Jerry. M. Linenger. McGraw-Hill, 2000.

## Preparation

- Schedule library time for research.
- Familiarize yourself with the general chronology of Russian space exploration.

## Group Size

Students will work in pairs or groups of three or four.

## OBJECTIVES

- Conduct research on Russia's space program, highlighting significant dates and achievements.

- Identify the many "firsts" Russia achieved in the field.

- Discuss why space exploration is important by looking at specific discoveries.

- Choose a specific part of Russia's space history and research the details.

- Present a time line of Russia's achievements in space.

## PROCEDURE

1. Begin with a class discussion about outer space. Ask students what comes to mind when they think of space exploration. Talk about NASA and the United States' space program. Then introduce the fact that Russia was a leader in many areas before the United States.

2. Distribute copies of **Student Handout 1: "Student Activity Outline."** Review what students will be required to do. Explain that they will research a period of time from Russia's history of space exploration. Have each pair or group choose a topic. If two pairs or groups choose the same topic, guide them to take a different approach so that everyone adds something unique to the class time line.

3. Distribute copies of **Student Handout 2: "The Importance of Space Exploration."** Point out that students will be required as part of their presentation to explain how their particular Russian achievement in space exploration betters the world.

4. Distribute copies of **Student Handout 3: "Comparing World Space Exploration."** Explain that students should research the achievements in space of other countries, especially the United States, to compare to the Russian program. Discuss how competition in technology worldwide can have both positive and negative outcomes.

5. Allow time for research. Each group should record its findings on all three handouts.

6. Schedule time for the preparation of their presentation. Hand out all materials necessary and explain that students can use computer printouts, written text, hand-drawn pictures, or computer-generated images to illustrate their portion of the class time line.

7. Schedule a day for the actual presentations. Encourage a brief question and answer period following each group's presentation. End with a class discussion about how Russia's space program has benefited Russia and the world.

## Extend

Find a documentary on space exploration and share it with the class.

**Russia and the Caucasus**   Interdisciplinary Project

## The Russian Space Program

# Student Activity Outline

You and your partner or group will prepare and deliver a presentation
on an important achievement of the Russian space program.

## WHAT TO DO

1. Use available library and Internet resources to find a general history or time line
   of the Russian space program. Decide what the most important achievements
   were and choose one for your group's topic. Note the date or dates that
   the achievement took place.

2. Research the achievement in depth. Take complete notes, remembering the five
   "W's"—who, what, where, when, and why. Note any other interesting details.

3. Research visuals you can use with your presentation.

## PUT IT ALL TOGETHER

Write a script for your presentation. Plan for it to be no longer than five
minutes. Practice reading your script and revise it as necessary.

Next, use the sheet of paper your teacher will give you to create your
portion of the class time line. On this paper, place your images, a
caption that briefly explains the achievement, and the date or dates
of the achievement.

**Russia and the Caucasus**                  Interdisciplinary Project

# The Importance of Space Exploration

The various space programs around the world cost billions of dollars every year. Is this expense worthwhile?

## THREE GOOD REASONS

There are many reasons for having a space program. Each reason usually falls into one of three categories:

**1.** survival

**2.** health, comfort, and convenience

**3.** increasing our knowledge about the universe

## YOUR ASSIGNMENT

As part of your presentation, your group must determine how the achievement you chose betters the world. Which of the three categories above does it fall under? For example, one reason we need space exploration to survive is the threat of a cosmic collision. After all, this may be the reason the dinosaurs became extinct. On the other hand, many of our everyday products are a direct result of the space program, such as computer software. In addition, to learn about the universe, we must explore it.

Use a chart like the one below to take notes about the achievement you are researching. Then decide which one reason best applies to that achievement.

| Survival | Health, Comfort, Convenience | Knowledge |
|---|---|---|
|  |  |  |

**Russia and the Caucasus**   Interdisciplinary Project

# Comparing World Space Exploration

During his administration, President George Bush gave the main space agency for the United States, NASA, a new focus for future space exploration. At a press conference, Bush said the first goal was to complete the International Space Station by the year 2010. The second goal was to develop and test a new spacecraft and conduct its first manned mission no later than 2014. The third goal was to return to the moon by 2020. Said Bush, "We'll invite other nations to share the challenges and opportunities of this new era of discovery . . . It is a journey, not a race, and I call on other nations to join us on this journey with a spirit of cooperation and friendship."

Meanwhile, Russia continued working on its space program. Said Russian President Vladimir Putin, "The rocket and space industry is not only a prestigious industrial branch which is making Russia a great power, but it is also an industry which deals with the most daring and reasonable economic projects."

## IS COMPETITION IN SPACE A GOOD THING?

Conduct additional research to investigate competition between countries in space exploration. For example, you may want to compare the achievement of the Russian and United States space programs at the same point in time. Or you may want to research areas of cooperation in space between Russia and the United States today.

Share your findings with the rest of the class. You may want to do this as part of your presentation or on a separate sheet of paper for display.

**Russia and the Caucasus**

# Interdisciplinary Project
## The Russian Space Program

# Standards for Evaluating Your Work

**EXCELLENT**

- The presentation included all required information.
- The presentation was well organized and thoroughly researched.
- The illustrated time line was very neatly done and included all required information.
- The presentation and time line involved every group member.

**GOOD**

- The presentation included most of the required information.
- The presentation demonstrated good research and organization.
- The illustrated time line was neatly done and included most of the required information.
- The presentation and time line involved most group members.

**ACCEPTABLE**

- The presentation included some of the required information.
- The presentation demonstrated some research and was fairly well organized.
- The illustrated time line was somewhat neatly done and included some of the required information.
- The presentation and time line involved some group members.

**UNACCEPTABLE**

- The presentation was missing significant amounts of required information.
- The presentation showed poor research and lack of organization.
- The illustrated time line was messy and lacked most of the required information.
- The presentation and time line involved only a few group members.

# Answer Key

## Holt Social Studies

# Europe and Russia

## Vocabulary Builder

### SECTION 1
1. T
2. F; golden age
3. F; Athens
4. F; Hellenistic
5. T

### SECTION 2
1. Rome
2. Senate
3. Citizens
4. republic
5. empire
6. aqueducts
7. Pax Romana

Students' poems or stories will vary, but should reflect correct usage of the terms.

### SECTION 3
1. Middle Ages
2. pope
3. Crusade
4. Holy Land
5. Gothic architecture
6. feudal system
7. manor
8. nation-state

Students' letters will vary, but should reflect correct usage of at least five terms in the word bank.

## Biography

### ALEXANDER THE GREAT

### WHAT DID YOU LEARN?
1. His father, the king, had been killed, so the army declared him the new ruler.
2. He was likely determined, intelligent, and fair. His army was loyal and well-trained, so he must have had their respect.

### ACTIVITY
Students' time lines will vary. Possible conquests to include: Meletus (334 BC), Issus (333 BC), Tyre (332 BC), and Jhelum (326 BC).

## Biography

### OCTAVIA THURINA MINOR

### WHAT DID YOU LEARN?
1. She cared for children and tried to keep peace in Rome.
2. Possible answer—to ensure that both families benefited from the union; to ensure that the Roman Empire benefited

### ACTIVITY
Students' monuments will vary, but should reflect the positive qualities of Octavia's character and her achievements.

## Literature

### CALL-OUT BOXES
1. possible answer—She may have married him because he was a great knight, or because he won her heart.
2. possible answer—The narrator seems likely to have been a peasant.

### ANALYZING LITERATURE
1. Theseus was a duke, the lord and governor of Athens, and a great conqueror.
2. Possible answer—Both conquered foreign lands and were respected leaders. However, Theseus is a fictional character while Alexander the Great is a historical figure.

### ACTIVITY
Students' poems or stories will vary, but should be similar in tone and structure to Chaucer's tale.

## Primary Source

### WHAT DID YOU LEARN?
1. Spain, Africa, and Germany
2. They wish to honor him for all his achievements.
3. Possible answer—humanitarian, because he restored peace to many lands; dictator, because he ruled absolutely over his colonies.

## Geography and History

### MAP ACTIVITY
The colors and shading on students' maps should be accurate and neat.

## ANALYZING MAPS

1. A direct land route might be fastest.
2. by sea, because it's shorter
3. Routes may have been determined by the landscapes, such as mountains.
4. robbers/pirates, language barriers, bad weather, difficult terrain
5. Knowing these may help people create more efficient or safer trade routes.

# Social Studies Skills

## PRACTICE THE SKILL

1. southeast          4. Mediterranean Sea
2. AD 1096–1099       5. France
3. about 400 miles

## APPLY THE SKILL

Possible questions—What are two major battle sites? What major bodies of water did the empire border?

# Geography for Life

Possible answers:
1. Travel today is generally faster and safer, but it still has dangers, as in the past.
2. Europeans came into contact with new technology from the Muslims.
3. 125 hours; about 15 days; by foot, because you could see more and meet more people; by train, because it is faster and easier
4. by sea, it seems faster; by land, it seems safer and might cost less
5. pirates, bandits, or raiders of the future; finding a reliable source of fuel

# Critical Thinking

1. northeasterly direction to north-central France; Paris correctly placed
2. Antioch and Budapest correctly placed; route should move north, cross the Black Sea, then move due west for 200–300 miles before turning north to Budapest
3. From top to bottom: summum dorsum, nucleus, rudus, statument, pavimentum, fossa
4. Answers will vary, but should note that paved roads allow troops to travel faster.

# Focus on Reading

Students' responses will vary, but should reflect an understanding of the main ideas and key supporting details from each section.

# Focus on Writing

Students' myths will vary, but should include characters, settings, and topics from the chapter. Myths should be written in the style of someome living during the time period discussed.

# Chapter Review

## REVIEWING VOCABULARY, TERMS, AND PLACES

1. city-states        6. facilitate
2. aqueducts          7. Hellenistic
3. pope               8. empire
4. manor              9. Holy Land
5. golden age        10. Middle Ages

## COMPREHENSION AND CRITICAL THINKING

1. republic           3. military leaders
2. Macedonia

## REVIEWING THEMES

1. place, because the Parthenon is associated with Athens, Greece, where it was built and still stands
2. Greek trading ships, Roman roads, horses in the Crusades

## REVIEW ACTIVITY: ADVERTISEMENT

Ads will vary, but should include at least six key historical events from before AD 1500. Ads should be based on facts in the chapter, and they should be persuasive and attractive.

# Interdisciplinary Project

## RESEARCH PROJECT: THE BLACK DEATH

Students' presentations will vary, but can be evaluated with the rubric on the Student Handout, "Standards for Evaluating Your Work."

## Vocabulary Builder

### SECTION 1

1. F; Renaissance
2. T
3. F; perspective

4. F; Venice
5. F; humanism

Students' stories and poems will vary, but should reflect an appropriate use of the vocabulary words.

### SECTION 2

1. Galileo
2. Scientific Revolution
3. Queen Isabella
4. Vasco da Gama
5. Sir Isaac Newton
6. ship
7. go around
8. navigation aid
9. uses reason
10. force that attracts objects

### SECTION 3

1. Possible answer—Parliament approved the English Bill of Rights to protect people's rights.
2. Possible answer—The National Assembly wrote a constitution called the Declaration of the Rights of Man and of the Citizen.
3. Possible answer—Colonists questioned their government; The American Revolution began; the Declaration of Independence was signed in July 1776.
4. Possible answer—the Reign of Terror; it relates to the beheading of so many people.
5. Possible answer—The Congress of Vienna, which reshaped the map of Europe.

### SECTION 4

1. c
2. a
3. d
4. c
5. c

6. economic system, free enterprise, individuals own businesses
7. fabrics, cloths, clothing
8. woman campaigning for the right to vote, British woman seeking equality, woman seeking political power

9. period of rapid growth in machine-made goods, in the mid-1700s, when machines changed how people lived and worked
10. use of inventions, ways of making products, ways of using resources

## Biography

### GALILEO

### WHAT DID YOU LEARN?

1. Possible answer—Galileo used his telescope to observe the night sky. His observations gave him evidence that Earth revolved around the sun.
2. Possible answer—Galileo is known as the father of modern astronomy because he made improvements to the telescope. As a result, he and others made new discoveries about the moon, sun, Earth, and other planets.

### ACTIVITY

Questions will vary. Examples: What did you learn about the moon and planets using your telescope? Why do you think your ideas were controversial? Why did you continue to work while under house arrest?

## Biography

### NAPOLEON BONAPARTE

### WHAT DID YOU LEARN?

1. Possible answer—Napoleon became emperor of France and established the Napoleonic Code.
2. Possible answers—Napoleon reformed the French government after the French Revolution. He worked to expand the French empire.

### ACTIVITY

Students' time lines will vary, but should include key events, such as Napoleon becoming emperor and his defeats in Russia and at Waterloo.

## Literature

### CALL-OUT BOXES

1. The way the creature looks disgusts him.
2. Circled words may include *yellow skin, watery eyes, shrivelled complexion.*

### ANALYZING LITERATURE

1. Frankenstein is excited and disgusted.
2. Shelley may have felt that technology could be used for good—or for evil.
3. Answers will vary, but students should note that he cannot truly escape from his creation.

### ACTIVITY

Pictures will vary but should include some of the physical attributes described in the excerpt.

## Primary Source

### WHAT DID YOU LEARN?

1. He says you should begin with "the details of them."
2. Answers will vary. Students may say that examining details first can apply to science and architecture because details are important in these studies.

## Geography and History

### MAP ACTIVITY

1. Maps should show labels for Spain, South America, Asia, Africa, Atlantic Ocean, Pacific Ocean, and Indian Ocean.
2. Colors will vary, but should be accurate.
3. Map legends should accurately reflect colors on map.

### ANALYZING MAPS

1. South America
2. Strait of Magellan
3. Atlantic Ocean, Pacific Ocean, Indian Ocean
4. It helped people learn more about the world; it opened up new ocean routes.

## Social Studies Skills

### PRACTICE THE SKILL

Students' chart will vary, but should show an understanding of benefits/trade-offs associated with each possible choice and of the trade-off.

### APPLY THE SKILL

Answers will vary but should show knowledge and understanding of trade-off.

## Geography for Life

Possible answers:

1. Different—more people can vote today; similar—people still move to the city from the country today.
2. They may have moved for better jobs and to have a chance at becoming wealthy.
3. It is still common for people to leave the country and go to the city for education or a chance at earning more money.
4. artist in an Italian city; chances to earn fame and wealth seems better in the city
5. The city would be bustling, with people selling their wares. My home would be small, but comfortable. I'd know a lot of my neighbors.

## Critical Thinking

Possible answers:

1. Neither—both present just one side; the true story is likely a combination of both viewpoints.
2. not wanting to interfere; No, because the act did interfere with the workers meeting.
3. The factory would be safe and as pleasant as a factory could be. Workers would have a shorter day and be treated better. Business may actually go up, if workers are more motivated.
4. No—because it supports poor business practices; Yes—it's up to the workers to change their situation.
5. Our government could enforce regulations fairly and have regular inspections. Our trade policies could depend on how well another country treats its workers.

## Focus on Reading

Students' time lines will vary, but should include key events, in order by date, from each section of the textbook chapter.

## Focus on Writing

Students' travel brochures will vary, but should be well-organized, factual, and neat, and should meet rubric standards.

## Chapter Review

### REVIEWING VOCABULARY, TERMS, AND PLACES

1. Renaissance
2. Reformation
3. circumnavigate
4. Galileo
5. Enlightenment
6. capitalism
7. suffragettes
8. contract

### COMPREHENSION AND CRITICAL THINKING

1. a; false
2. b; false
3. b; false
4. a; false
5. b; false

### REVIEWING THEMES

1. place
2. movement
3. human-environment interaction

### REVIEW ACTIVITY: JOURNAL ENTRY

Students' journal entries will vary but should include a description of their physical location and of significant events from the time period they selected.

## Vocabulary Builder

### SECTION 1

possible answers:

1. *Nationalism* created growing tensions between European countries and caused WWI.
2. The *Allies*, which consisted of Serbia, Britain, France, Russia, and later the United States, fought against the *Central Powers*, led by Austria-Hungary and Germany.
3. *Trench warfare* created a *stalemate* in the war and exposed the soldiers to constant danger, cold, hunger, and disease.
4. The *Treaty of Versailles* demanded that Germany accept blame for the war, slash the size of its army, give up overseas colonies, and pay billions of dollars for damage.
5. Some countries were governed by *communism*

An alliance is a group of nations that have joined together to advance and defend its goals.

### SECTION 2

1. F; Axis Powers
2. T
3. F; dictator
4. T
5. T
6. F; Allies

Definitions may vary but should be appropriate for each term selected.

### SECTION 3

1. Cold War
2. reunification
3. ethnic tensions
4. European Union
5. arms race

possible answer—During the *Cold War*, the two *superpowers* competed in an *arms race*. *Ethnic tensions* transformed Eastern Europe. To promote a *common market*, many nations joined the *European Union (EU)*.

## Biography

### ANNE FRANK

### WHAT DID YOU LEARN?

1. possible answer—Anne Frank and her family went into hiding in an attic to escape persecution by the Nazis. They were discovered in 1944. Anne, her mother, and sister all died in the Holocaust. Anne's diary was published after her death.
2. Answers will vary. Some students may note her detailed description of life in hiding. Other students may mention her optimism despite her situation.

### ACTIVITY

Epitaphs may reflect Anne's optimism, hopefulness, talkativeness, or bravery.

## Biography

### VLADIMIR LENIN

### WHAT DID YOU LEARN?

1. classless society, no individual ownership of land and property
2. Students may focus on the proletariat point of view (Lenin would be popular) or on the upper class point of view (probably not popular).

### ACTIVITY

Speeches will vary, but should focus on Lenin's belief that power will be given back to the workers (proletariat) and that there will no longer be such differences in lifestyle between the wealthy and the poor.

## Literature

### CALL-OUT BOX

1. possible answer—Pigs and dogs are bigger and hungrier than other animals.
2. because *reduction* is a more negative word
3. "harsh and bare," "often hungry and often cold," "usually working"

## ANALYZING LITERATURE

1. possible answer—Animalism has not been successful because life is harsh and unfair for most of the animals.
2. Students should infer that Squealer is either a pig or dog because his rations haven't been reduced; based on his name, he is most likely a pig.

## ACTIVITY

Allegories will vary but should show thought in their choice of animals to represent democratic and Communist governments.

## Primary Source

### WHAT DID YOU LEARN?

1. possible answer—Three goals of the United Nations are to maintain peace, protect human rights, and promote tolerance.
2. possible answer—The United Nations might have prevented the competition for land, resources, and power that led to WWI.
3. possible answers—terrorism or ethnic problems in the Middle East or Africa.

## Geography and History

### MAP ACTIVITY

1. Allied Powers include Serbia, Russia, France, Italy, and Great Britain.
2. Central Powers include Germany and Austria-Hungary.
3. Spain and Switzerland were neutral.

### ANALYZING MAPS

1. St. Petersburg is located on the Western border of Russia, near Finland.
2. possible answer—Controlling France and Belgium would give Germany easy access to the Atlantic Ocean.
3. possible answer—The Allied Powers had an advantage because they surrounded Germany, which had to fight the war on two fronts.
4. The United States' challenges included the distance they had to travel to get soldiers and supplies to the war. This was also ... advantage, as their land was not in ...diate danger of invasion.

5. possible answers: same—Some countries, such as Spain, had the same borders; different—many countries lost or gained territory, and new countries were created.

## Social Studies Skills

1. The cartoon was likely published at the time Hitler and Stalin had agreed not to attack each other (in 1939, before World War II broke out).
2. possible answer—They both look happy, as if they will be partners for a long time.
3. possible answer—Although the picture shows them happy together, the caption suggests that their honeymoon, or partnership, will not last.

## Geography for Life

Students' reports should accurately reflect their research.

1. Gagarin
2. Luhansk
3. Volgograd
4. St. Petersburg
5. Pushkin
6. Gatchina
7. Nizhniy Novgorod
8. Perm
9. Naberezhnyye Chelny
10. Engels

## Critical Thinking

1. The Polish farmers were in the area of heaviest fallout, while the East Germans were not. Although the Swedes were also in the heavy fallout pattern, they were farther from the accident, so the radiation would have been more diffused.
2. On April 27, the wind blew to the northwest, as shown by the fallout pattern on the next day, April 28. By April 29, the wind had shifted toward the southwest, as shown by the fallout pattern for April 30, in which the cloud has extended southwest.

**3.** Northern Italy; even though the map shows that the cloud for both April 30 (over northern Italy) and for May 3 (over southern England) ranged between 1 and 10 mrems of radiation, the May 3 cloud covered a much larger region, meaning the radiation in that area would have been more diffused—more on the lower end of the 1-to-10 mrem scale—than the radiation in the cloud that blanketed northern Italy on April 30, which was likely on the upper end of that scale.

# Focus on Reading

**1.** Students should use the clue *length* to arrive at their definition of *zigzag*.

**2.** Students should use the clue *accepting* to arrive at their definition of *discriminating*.

**3.** Students should use the clue *rather than oppose* to arrive at their definition of *advocated*.

# Focus on Writing

**1.** Students may choose any event from WWI, including a trench warfare battle (told from the point of view of a German or French soldier), or a German U-boat attack (told from the point of view of a British sailor on a ship).

**2.** Events from WWII might include life under the dictatorship of Mussolini, Stalin, or Hitler, or the Holocaust.

**3.** Details about Europe after 1945 might include the formation of the United Nations, the Cold War, the threat of nuclear war, or the European Union.

Diary entries will vary but should be descriptive and accurate. The rubric can be used to evaluate diary entries.

# Chapter Review

## REVIEWING VOCABULARY, TERMS, AND PLACES

**1.** nationalism     **4.** dictator

**2.** trench warfare     **5.** Cold War

**3.** Holocaust

## COMPREHENSION AND CRITICAL THINKING

**1.** alliance          **4.** Nazi

**2.** Serbia           **5.** government

**3.** Great Depression

## REVIEWING THEMES

possible answers:

**1.** Nationalism is often tied to a region's shared characteristics—language, religion, and history. For example, nationalism led some people in Bosnia and Herzegovina, a region in southeastern Europe, to demand independence. This devotion to one's country, or region, led to conflict and rivalry in Europe.

**2.** The Treaty of Versailles, which was the final peace settlement of World War I, changed many regions of Europe. The new political borders divided many people and regions in Europe.

**3.** The Berlin Wall was built to stop the flow of people from Communist East Berlin to democratic West Berlin.

**4.** The European Union was created in large part to ensure the easy movement of goods and people within Europe's borders.

## REVIEW ACTIVITY: TIME LINE

Students' time lines should cover all major events from WWI, WWII, and the Cold War. They should include at least two maps; one to show Europe pre-WWI, and one post-WWI. They could include a map to show the countries of the European Union.

# Interdisciplinary Project

## READING AND WRITING ALLEGORIES

Students' allegories will vary, but can be evaluated with the rubric.

## CURRENT EVENTS

Students should show an understanding of the current issue they are discussing as well as their historical character.

# Vocabulary Builder

## SECTION 1

1. F; Pyrenees
2. T
3. F; Alps
4. F, Mediterranean sea
5. F; Apennines
6. undersea mountains
7. Mediterranean climate

## SECTION 2

1. representative, government, free elections
2. government, king, ruler
3. idea, reason, ancient Greece
4. religion
5. Parthenon

Students' summaries should use five words from the word bank and accurately reflect section content.

## SECTION 3

1. Nationalism
2. pope
3. Vatican City
4. Rome
5. Sicily
6. Milan

Students' poems, stories, or letters should include at least five terms from the section.

## SECTION 4

1. The Portuguese sing sad folk songs called *fados*; the Spanish are known for a style of song and dance called *flamenco*.
2. Spain is ruled by a *parliamentary monarchy* in which the king rules with the help of an elected parliament; Portugal is a *republic* whose leaders are elected.
3. *Madrid* and *Barcelona* are centers of industry, tourism, and culture in Spain.
4. Portugal's industries are based in *Lisbon* and other cities.
5. d
6. d

# Biography

## ARISTOTLE

### WHAT DID YOU LEARN?

1. Anti-Macedonian feelings broke out in Athens, and he feared for his life.

2. Answers will vary, but students may mention his contributions to the fields of philosphy, logic, meteorology, zoology, religion, and government.

### ACTIVITY

Students' descriptions will vary based on what they chose to observe.

# Biography

## AMÁLIA RODRIGUES

### WHAT DID YOU LEARN?

1. possible answer—She used her misfortunes as a challenge and refused to give up.
2. possible answers—She was an international star; she recorded over 50 albums; she was also a film star.

### ACTIVITY

Epitaphs may vary but should include details from the reading.

# Literature

## CALL-OUT BOX

Students should underline "thirty or more monstrous giants," "so evil a breed," and "long arms, some of them nearly two leagues long" for what Don quixote sees and "windmills" and "the vanes that turned by the wind make the millstone go" for what Sancho Panza sees.

## ANALYZING LITERATURE

1. Answers may include Don Quixote's stubborness and refusal to listen to reason.
2. possible answers—He thinks very highly of himself; he is delusional.

### ACTIVITY

Students should include humor and exaggeration in the dialogue of their skits.

# Primary Source

## WHAT DID YOU LEARN?

1. Answers may vary, but most will say he is portraying God as all-knowing.
2. possible answers—a soul, intellect

**3.** possible answer—The muscular forms of the individuals and the outline of the human brain illustrate a knowledge of science while the religious content reflects an interest in classical values.

# Geography and History
## MAP ACTIVITY
**1.** Students should draw a boundary between northern and southern Italy at the capital city of Rome.
**2.** Students should use a bright color to highlight Naples, Rome, Milan, Turin, and Genoa.
**3.** Students should use a light color to highlight Rome, Florence, Pisa, and Venice.
**4.** Students should shade the Po Valley.
**5.** Students should add to the map legend colors and labels for industry and trade, tourism, and agriculture.

## ANALYZING MAPS
**1.** in northern Italy
**2.** Rome
**3.** The region has many rivers.
**4.** Italy's peninsula location and major rivers have facilitated transportation and trade.
**5.** Climate is important to both tourism and agriculture in Italy.

# Social Studies Skills

Students should sketch a map of their region of the United States and write a brief description of the average weather conditions, including seasonal changes.

# Geography For Life

Students' maps should include all the underscored words in the activity.

# Critical Thinking
**1.** Answers may vary, but students should give reasons to support their opinions.

**2.** human intervention—factories built outside of Venice pumped water from underground, global warming, digging deep shipping channels eroded building foundations; nature—rising tides
**3.** Answers may vary, but students should give reasons to support their opinions.
**4.** People are leaving because the city floods so often.
**5.** possible answer—It is located on the water at the beginning of the peninsula.
**6.** Answers will vary.

# Focus on Reading
**1.** Italians
**2.** They formed their own states.
**3.** Italy
**4.** AD 400s
**5.** because of weak leadership and outside invasions

# Focus on Writing

Students' reports will vary, but should include the highlights from the chapter by utilizing the notes they took in the prewriting exercise. They should be detailed and accurate.

# Chapter Review
## REVIEWING VOCABULARY, TERMS, AND PLACES
**1.** the climate found across southern Europe characterized by warm, dry summers and mild, wet winters
**2.** modern
**3.** a separate state within Rome, Italy, where the Pope, the head of the Roman Catholic Church resides
**4.** something that leads people to follow a certain course of action
**5.** a sad Portuguese folk song
**6.** the westernmost peninsula in Europe (shared by Spain and Portugal)
**7.** a branch of Christianity that dates back to the Byzantine Empire
**8.** Europe's highest mountain range, found in the north

Europe and Russia

## COMPREHENSION AND CRITICAL THINKING

1. b, d, c, a
2. d, a, c, b
3. c, a, d, b

## REVIEWING THEMES

1. place
2. region
3. human/environment interaction

## REVIEW ACTIVITY: TRAVEL BROCHURE

Students should capture the essence of Southern Europe by using much of the vocabulary in the chapter, listing historical facts, addressing climate and geography, daily life (food, music), and highlighting important cities in Greece, Italy, Spain and Portugal.

# Vocabulary Builder

## SECTION 1

1. T
2. F; Danube and Rhine
3. T
4. F; North Sea
5. F; English Channel

Directions will vary but should reflect an understanding of the section terms.

## SECTION 2

1. Impressionism
2. Paris
3. dikes
4. cosmopolitan
5. Amsterdam
6. enjoyment of life
7. Mediterranean seaport
8. seat of government in the Netherlands
9. capital of Belgium
10. term to define Belgium, the Netherlands, and Luxembourg

## SECTION 3

1. Berlin
2. chancellor
3. cantons
4. Vienna
5. Bern

Students' summaries will vary but should include five terms from the word bank.

# Biography

## JACQUES-YVES COUSTEAU

### WHAT DID YOU LEARN?

1. Possible answer—Cousteau's films helped educate the public about environmental problems happening around the world.
2. Possible answer—Yes. Cousteau's films helped educate the public about ocean life in a way that was easy to understand.

### ACTIVITY

Students' collages will vary but should include relevant pictures of ocean life.

# Biography

## EMMY NOETHER

### WHAT DID YOU LEARN?

1. Possible answer—because she was a woman

2. Possible answer—She may have inspired other women to pursue careers in traditionally "male-only" careers.

### ACTIVITY

Students' job descriptions should reflect an understanding of the qualifications, training, tools, and job duties of a mathematician.

# Literature

## ANALYZING LITERATURE

1. studying plant life
2. Possible answer—He is highly aware because he is able to observe and comment on every detail of nature that comes into his view such as flowers.

### ACTIVITY

Students' descriptions will vary but should use vivid details to describe each image.

# Primary Source

## WHAT DID YOU LEARN?

Possible answers:

1. It is the tallest bridge in the world; transparent screens protect vehicles from wind.
2. He believes that the bridge is a beautiful and magnificent work that will last a long time.
3. Driving across the bridge is like flying through the Tarn Valley.

# Geography and History

## MAP ACTIVITY

1. Belgium, France, Germany, Italy, Luxembourg, and the Netherlands should be the same color.
2. Austria, Denmark, Finland, Greece, Ireland, Portugal, Spain, Sweden, and the United Kingdom should be the same color.
3. Cyprus, Czech Republic, Estonia, Hungary, Latvia, Lithuania, Malta, Poland, Slovakia, and Slovenia should be the same color.
4. Legends should match colors on maps.

## INTERPRETING MAPS

1. Belgium, France, Germany, Italy, Luxembourg, the Netherlands
2. United Kingdom, Ireland, Malta
3. Poland
4. Luxembourg

**5.** Possible answer—Yes. The EU allows Europeans more freedom to work, live, trade, study, and travel within Europe.

## Social Studies Skills

### PRACTICE THE SKILL
**1.** 23.5%          **3.** 76.0%
**2.** 0.5%           **4.** permanent crops

## Geography for Life

**1.** All 25 EU countries should be correctly labeled on the map.
**2.** green—Belgium, the Netherlands, Luxembourg, Germany, France, Italy; blue—Britain, Ireland, Denmark; purple—Greece; orange—Spain, Portugal; yellow—Austria, Sweden, Finland; red stripes—Cyprus, Czech Republic, Estonia, Hungary, Latvia, Lithuania, Malta, Poland, Slovakia, Slovenia.
**3.** horizontal stripes—Belgium, Canada, Denmark, France, Iceland, Italy, Luxembourg, the Netherlands, Norway, Portugal, the United Kingdom, the United States; vertical stripes—Greece, Turkey, Germany, Spain; diagonal stripes—Poland, Hungary, Czech Republic; dots—Bulgaria, Estonia, Latvia, Lithuania, Romania, Slovakia, Slovenia.
**4.** Maps should have a title and a key.
**5.** Students' findings will vary.

## Critical Thinking

**1.** possible answer—It limited ingredients to what could be raised or caught locally. Four regions are described.
**2.** possible answer—chestnut or corn flour, and lentils and beans
**3.** possible answer—more typical of Marseilles, because it's a fish-based soup
**4.** possible answer—Reims, because both are in the traditional cattle-raising regions of France
**5.** possible answer—Food in Nice would focus on goat meat and fish prepared with olive oil, herbs, tomatoes, peppers, garlic, and citrus fruits. Foods in Tours would focus on beef, dairy products, and fruits and vegetables.

## Focus on Reading

### SECTION 1
Possible answer: Massif—mountainous mass broken up into separate peaks; French

### SECTION 2
**1.** impressionism          **3.** café
**2.** joie de vivre          **4.** low lands.

### SECTION 3
Possible answers—Oktoberfest, Beethoven

### RECOGNIZING LATIN ROOTS
Possible answers:
**1.** imaginary—*ary* is the adjective-forming suffix meaning "related to."
**2.** revolution—*ion* means "the act or condition of."
**3.** Reunification—*re* means "redo or repeat."

## Focus on Speaking

Students' speeches should clearly identify the issue and their position toward it, and be presented in a persuasive manner.

## Chapter Review

### REVIEWING VOCABULARY, TERMS, AND PLACES
**1.** navigable          **5.** Brussels
**2.** impressionism      **6.** purpose
**3.** Paris              **7.** chancellor
**4.** dikes              **8.** neutral

### COMPREHENSION AND CRITICAL THINKING
**1.** Massif Central      **3.** Switzerland
**2.** Amsterdam

### REVIEWING THEMES
**1.** Navigable rivers allow for travel and trade.
**2.** The European Union allows for movement across borders with few restrictions.
**3.** The Berlin Wall prevented movement between West Berlin and East Berlin.

### REVIEW ACTIVITY: TIME LINE
Students should focus on key events from the chapter. Each event should have a visual.

## Vocabulary Builder

### SECTION 1
1. glaciers
2. Scandinavia
3. fjord
4. geothermal energy
5. North Atlantic Drift
6. b
7. d
8. d
9. d

### SECTION 2
1. Industrial Revolution
2. agreement
3. Stonehenge
4. constitutional monarchy
5. disarm
6. capital of UK, center of world trade, largest city in British Isles
7. Ireland's capital, computer and software industries, located on the coast
8. Great Charter, limited king's power, ordered everyone to obey the law

### SECTION 3
Possible responses:
1. The *Vikings* used quick and powerful longboats to attack and conquer villages.
2. Eighty percent of Greenland is covered by ice, so much of the land is *uninhabitable*.
3. Sweden has been a *neutral* country for almost 200 years.
4. They are heated with geothermal energy from *hot springs* and *geysers*.
5. *Stockholm*, Sweden, is built on 14 islands and part of the mainland.

## Biography

### MARY, QUEEN OF SCOTS

### WHAT DID YOU LEARN?
1. possible answer—Her choices made her unpopular with the people of Scotland and led to her being forced to give up the throne.
2. possible answer—With Queen Elizabeth out of the picture, Mary hoped to become Queen of England.

### ACTIVITY
Students should create a detailed family tree showing Mary Stuart's relations to other rulers.

## Biography

### HANS CHRISTIAN ANDERSEN

### WHAT DID YOU LEARN?
1. possible answer—He met Jonas Collin, who helped him get the money to continue his education.
2. possible answer—He was born into poverty and had a difficult childhood, but through determination and perseverance he became successful and famous.

### ACTIVITY
Answers will vary, but students' interviews should relate details from Andersen's life to one of his fairy tales.

## Literature

### CALL-OUT BOXES
1. Montague; Capulet
2. She means that a rose would still have the same qualities if it were called something else, just as Romeo would.
3. If Juliet agrees to love him, he will use a new name.

## ANALYZING LITERATURE

1. They are in love, but their families are enemies.
2. Students may answer that they will have to hide their relationship or that they will end their relationship out of fear for Romeo's life.

### Activity

Students should show an understanding of both iambic pentameter and the sonnet form in their poems.

# Primary Source

## WHAT DID YOU LEARN?

1. a fjord
2. possible answers—scared, shocked, anxious, tired, sad, aliented, lonely
3. possible answer—very thin, unrealistic
4. possible answer—Nature is distorted to represent the main figure's emotions.

# Geography and History

## MAP ACTIVITY

1. Students should color England, Scotland, Wales, and Northern Ireland yellow.
2. Students should color Sweden, Denmark, Norway, Finland, and Iceland green.
3. Students should outline at least three fjords in red; most are located on Norway's west coast.
4. Students should place an "X" on the British Isles, northern France, Finland, Iceland, Norway, Germany, Russia, and Sweden.

## ANALYZING MAPS

1. about 1200 miles
2. It is part of Ireland geographically, but part of the United Kingdom politically.
3. Its longitude extends from about 10° E to about 25° W. Its latitude extends from about 50° N to about 75° N.
4. Glaciers in the Arctic Ocean account for the jagged west coast. The east coast is enclosed by the Baltic Sea and Gulf of Bothnia, so glaciers had less access, making it a straighter coastline.

# Social Studies Skills

## PRACTICE THE SKILL

Students' recall (in any order or form) is more important than the writing structure. However, notes should show evidence of freestyle writing for the full 15 minutes.

# Geography for Life

1. Denmark, Norway, Sweden
2. They went west from the Faeroe Islands.
3. They went south from Denmark and Sweden.
4. They went to Eastern Europe, Russia, and Asia from Sweden.
5. The latest date on the map is 1190 in the Norman Kingdom in what is now Italy.

Students' essays should demonstrate an understanding of the major issues involved in migration discussed in the activity.

# Critical Thinking

1. Answers will vary but should focus on the fact that the Chunnel physically connects Britain to the continent of Europe, effectively ending its isolation.
2. Answers will vary but should show recognition of the headline's suggestion of total isolation from the European mainland.
3. Answers will vary, but students should recognize that the marl was softer than the chalk, which made tunneling easier, but harder than clay or sand, so it provides some rigidity and support for the tunnel.
4. The drawing shows several fault lines. A major shift along any of these faults could warp or snap the tunnel and thus shut it down for a long period, or even permanently.

# Focus on Reading

## PRACTICING USING CONTEXT CLUES

1. long, winding channels
2. energy produced from the heat of Earth's interior
3. an ancient monument
4. heritage
5. the capital of Norway
6. not able to support human settlement

## CREATING YOUR OWN CONTEXT CLUES

Sentences will vary but should show an understanding of the use of context clues.

# Focus on Writing

Letters should include information about the geography, history, and culture of Northern Europe, as well as students' reactions to their visit to the region.

# Chapter Review

## REVIEWING VOCABULARY, TERMS, AND PLACES

**Across:**

2. geothermal
5. Drift
6. London
7. Vikings
8. Parliament

**Down:**

1. Stockholm
2. geyser
3. fjord
4. Oslo

## COMPREHENSION AND CRITICAL THINKING

1. timber and fish
2. Scandinavia
3. culture
4. religious
5. peaceful

## REVIEWING THEMES

1. human-environment interaction
2. place
3. region

## REVIEW ACTIVITY: TRAVEL BROCHURE

Brochures should cover the information about Northern Europe in an organized, logical way. Pictures should highlight key stops during the cruise. Brochures should be attractive and persuasive.

## Vocabulary Builder

### SECTION 1
1. F; Carpathians
2. F; Adriatic Sea
3. T
4. T
5. F; Balkan Peninsula

### SECTION 2
1. infrastructure
2. Poland
3. Warsaw
4. Baltic Republics
5. Embroidery

Students' stories should correctly use at least four terms from the word bank and should relate to Poland or the Baltic Republics.

### SECTION 3
1. Commonwealth of Independent States
2. Magyars
3. Prague
4. Kiev
5. Slavs

Students' definitions will vary but should be consistent with section content.

### SECTION 4
1. d
2. c
3. b
4. a
5. a

Students' summaries should use at least three vocabulary terms to describe the diverse ethnic make-up and troubled history of the Balkans.

## Biography

### ESTÉE LAUDER

#### WHAT DID YOU LEARN?
1. free demonstrations, free samples, and promotional gifts with a purchase
2. creativity, determination, intelligence, persuasiveness, good communicator, strong business sense, hard worker; explanations will vary

#### ACTIVITY
Students' lists will vary, but should reflect evidence of research.

## Biography

### MADELEINE ALBRIGHT

#### WHAT DID YOU LEARN?
1. staff member on the National Security Council, co-founder of the Center for National Policy, U.S. Ambassador to the United Nations, member of President Clinton's cabinet, U.S. Secretary of State
2. She experienced Nazi and Communist governments firsthand; she spoke many different languages; she understood foreign relations because she was an immigrant herself.

#### ACTIVITY
Students' speeches should list Albright's accomplishments and positive qualities.

## Literature

### CALL-OUT BOX
*great, clean-cut, stone, eleven wide sweeping arches*

### ANALYZING LITERATURE
1. united the two parts of the Sarajevo road; linked the town and surrounding villages; was an indispensable link between Bosnia and Serbia; was a crossing for the Drina
2. possible answers—The towns would become isolated; travel between the two would only be possible by water; people might move, and the towns would shrink.

### ACTIVITY
Students may mention the Golden Gate Bridge connecting San Francisco and Oakland or one of the bridges linking the New York islands.

## Primary Source

### CALL-OUT BOX
The revolt was supported by many Hungarians.

### WHAT DID YOU LEARN?
1. disapproval; words such as *sabotage, infiltrate, undermine,* and *demands*

Europe and Russia

2. possible answer—Yes, because the people of Hungary should be able to decide on their own government leaders and should not be forced to live under Soviet rule.

3. Answers will vary, but students should give logicals reasons to support their answers.

# Geography and History

## MAP ACTIVITY

1. Refer students to the political map in Section 2 of their textbooks for accuracy in labeling the countries.

2. Countries shaded yellow should be Estonia, Latvia, Lithuania, Belorussia, Ukraine, Moldova, Romania, and Albania.

3. Countries shaded light blue should be Bulgaria, Yugoslavia, Hungary, Czechoslovakia, East Germany, and Poland.

5. Students' map legends should accurately reflect the colors on their maps.

## ANALYZING MAPS

1. Yugoslavia; Slovenia, Croatia, Bosnia and Herzegovina, Serbia and Montenegro, Macedonia

2. Albania, Macedonia, Slovenia, Croatia, Bulgaria, Bosnia and Herzegovina, Serbia and Montenegro, and Romania

3. Several Eastern European countries shared a border with the Soviet Union, which made it easier for Soviet troops to invade them. Once Soviets gained control of one area, they used their location to invade even more neighboring countries.

# Social Studies Skills

## PRACTICE THE SKILL

possible answers: benefits—independence, religious freedom; costs—violence, fewer shared resources

## APPLY THE SKILL

possible answers: benefits—potential for many paying passengers, contributing to Budapest's economy; costs—boat; fuel

# Geography for Life

1. Students' labels should show correct placement and spelling of countries' names.

2. Students' maps should show correct placement and spelling of labels for rivers and tributaries and correct highlighting of waterways.

3. Students' maps should show correct placement and spelling of labels for capital cities.

4. Sofia, Bucharest, Budapest, Belgrade, Sarajevo, Ljubljana, Zagreb, Vienna, and Bratislava

5. Prague, Berlin

6. Warsaw

7. Tirane, Skopje

8. The Elbe flows north and empties into the North Sea. Barge traffic slowed to a mere trickle after the Iron Curtain.

9. The Danube flows mainly west to east. It empties into the Black Sea. Traffic on the Rhine is greater than on the Danube because the Rhine flows through much wealthier countries in the heart of Europe.

10. The Rhine-Main-Danube Canal has increased commerce for the cities on its banks.

# Critical Thinking

1. Croats

2. 1991—Bosnians; 1996—Serbs

3. The country became more segregated into areas by ethnicity. The areas of mixed settlement were much smaller.

4. It declined by 1.2 million people, or more than 25 percent. Possible reasons—ethnic cleansing, people voluntarily fleeing the violence, deaths resulting from the fighting in the civil war

5. Answers will vary, but students should point to the reduced mixed territory on the 1996 map and the population decline and redistribution that is shown by the table. (Muslims went from 44% of Bosnias's population in 1991 to 38% just four years later.)

## Focus on Reading

Possible problems—high unemployment and crime rates in Albania, ethnic fighting in Bosnia and Montenegro, poor leadership and economy in Romania, poor infrastructure in the Baltics; Students' solutions should be logical and realistic.

## Focus on Viewing

Students' visual reports should include information about physical and human features of the countries they selected. Students' posters should provide visual support for the information presented in their oral reports. Presentations should be given confidently and with a loud, clear voice. Students should also follow the guidelines for giving effective feedback on their classmates' presentations.

## Chapter Review

### REVIEWING VOCABULARY, TERMS, AND PLACES

1. Danube
2. Chernobyl
3. ethnic cleansing
4. infrastructure
5. Prague
6. Budapest
7. Carpathians
8. Warsaw

### COMPREHENSION AND CRITICAL THINKING

1. Balkan
2. Commonwealth of Independent States
3. Kiev

### REVIEWING THEMES

1. Most Eastern European countries were occupied by the Soviet Union, which was ruled by a Communist government, during the Cold War.
2. Since the collapse of the Soviet Union, the Czech Republic, Slovakia, Hungary, and Ukraine have become important industrialized centers.

### REVIEW ACTIVITY: BUSINESS PLAN

Students' business plans may suggest the use of industry, tourism, and agriculture. Students should support their business plans with factual information from the textbook chapter.

## Interdisciplinary Project

### RESEARCH PROJECT: EASTERN EUROPE'S ECONOMY

Students' presentations should include the required elements outlined on the student handouts. The visuals should support information given in the presentation. All group members should have an active role in the research, planning, creating, and presentation of information.

# Vocabulary Builder

## SECTION 1

1. Caucasus Mountains
2. Ural Mountains
3. Volga River
4. steppe
5. Siberia

Students' poems and stories will vary but should include four terms from the word bank.

## SECTION 2

1. a
2. c
3. d
4. b
5. d

Students' summaries will vary but should include five terms from the word bank.

## SECTION 3

1. St. Petersburg
2. smelters
3. F; Trans-Siberian Railroad
4. T
5. F; Chechnya

## SECTION 4

1. farming society, rural, Azerbaijan
2. capital of Azerbaijan, chief port, on Caspian Sea
3. Yerevan
4. Tbilisi
5. Azerbaijan
6. Armenia
7. Black Sea

# Biography

## CATHERINE THE GREAT

### WHAT DID YOU LEARN?

1. expanding Russia's empire; keeping Russia out of Europe's wars; building museums, schools, and a medical college
2. possible answer—yes, because he was too friendly with Russia's enemy and made other decisions that hurt Russia

### ACTIVITY

Students may ask how they could free Russia's serfs or why she divided up Poland.

# Biography

## GARRY KASPAROV

### WHAT DID YOU LEARN?

1. He learned how to play chess at an early age and went to a special school to become a better player.
2. possible answer—Playing against a computer is harder because it can analyze every move more quickly than a person.

### ACTIVITY

Responses will vary. Students should write several paragraphs about an aspect of the game of chess.

# Literature

## CALL-OUT BOX

1. "afraid"

## ANALYZING LITERATURE

1. The battle was lost, he sees the many dead and wounded soldiers, and he is afraid of getting shot.
2. possible answer—Tolstoy was likely anti-war because of the descriptions of great suffering and death the battle caused.

## ACTIVITY

Students' essays will vary but should include likenesses and differences of main ideas or characters.

# Primary Source

## WHAT DID YOU LEARN?

1. Since most people could not read, icons helped them to understand their religion.
2. It is not very realistic, but it draws you in and can teach you about certain aspects of Christianity.
3. possible answer—They are easy to understand and to use and can help simplify communication.

# Geography and History

## MAP ACTIVITY

1. Students' maps should show areas with over 50 colored red.
2. Students' maps should show areas with 30–50 colored orange.
3. Students' maps should show areas with 10–30 colored yellow.
4. Students' maps should show areas with under 10 colored blue.

## ANALYZING MAPS

1. because the Moscow region was likely more suited for agriculture, which meant that more serfs were needed for labor
2. These regions likely had less agricultural land and thus needed fewer serfs.
3. Much of Russia was not suited for agriculture so it was less populated and there was less need for labor.
4. Russian agriculture may have become more mechanized, allowing former serfs to supply new sources of labor for industry or for working to harness Russia's wealth of natural resources.

# Social Studies Skills

## PRACTICE THE SKILL

1. 28–33 percent
2. Murmansk
3. possible answer—Russia's urban populations may be getting older or even declining, so fewer children are being born.

# Geography for Life

1. cotton, vineyards, vegetables, fruit, wheat, dairying, tea, citrus fruit, tobacco, corn, silkworms; the Colchis gets more precipitation; used for irrigation
2. livestock raising, grains, fruit, vineyards, vegetables; vines, tree crops, and animals often do well in hilly areas
3. livestock on seasonal pastures; too cold in winter
4. Baku, Tbilisi, Gänca
5. Students' responses will vary based on the area in which they live.

# Critical Thinking

1. The first nuclear explosion produced by humans did not occur until 1945, when the first atomic bomb destroyed Hiroshima. The Tunguska event took place in 1908.
2. Early scientists were discouraged from investigating by the area's swampiness and remoteness, Later, the Cold War kept non-Russians out of the area until the 1990s.

# Focus on Reading

possible answers:
Moscow is the heart and soul of Russia.
St. Petersburg is Russia's Venice, reflecting Russia's openness to the west.
Volga is a major source of energy for Russia and home to many factories.
The Urals is a major site of mining and manufacturing.
Russia's heartland is home to most of Russia's people, its capital, and industry.

# Focus on Writing

Students' real estate ads will vary but should reflect the most important features of one location in Russia or the Caucasus, include descriptive details, and appeal to potential buyers.

# Chapter Review

## REVIEWING VOCABULARY, TERMS, AND PLACES

1. Siberia
2. steppe
3. Cyrillic
4. gulags
5. Kremlin
6. Volga
7. Tbilisi
8. agrarian

## COMPREHENSION AND CRITICAL THINKING

1. Azerbaijan
2. taiga
3. Ivan the Terrible (Ivan IV)
4. communist
5. Trans-Siberian Railroad
6. ethnic

## REVIEWING THEMES

1. possible answer—Because Siberia has a harsh climate, few people have moved there even though it has a wealth of resources.

2. possible answer—The Volga River is a main transportation and shipping route.

## REVIEW ACTIVITY: FLASH CARDS

Students' flash cards should include at least three terms from each section and have correct definitions for each.

# Interdisciplinary Project

Students' time lines should describe an achievement in Russia's space history, the date(s) that the achievement took place, an explanation of how the achievement betters the world, and an illustration to accompany the achievement.